C000254789

THE
SYLVAC
Illustrated
COLLECTORS HANDBOOK

By Anthony Van Der Woerd

Georgian Publications
PO Box 1449,
Bath, BA1 2FF

ISBN 0 9521811 26

Copyright, Anthony Van Der Woerd. 2003
All rights reserved. No part of this publication
may be reproduced, stored in a retrieval system, or
transmitted, in any form or by any means, electronic,
mechanical, photocopying recording or otherwise,
without the prior permission of the copyright owner.

Important Notice

All information in this book has been compiled from reliable sources and every effort has been made to eliminate errors and questionable data. Nevertheless, the possibility of a mistake always exists. The author cannot, accordingly, be held responsible for losses which may occur in the purchase, sale or other transactions by reason of any information contained herein or indirectly attributable to the contents of this work. Readers who feel they have discovered errors or would like to offer further information or suggestions or provide photographs are invited to write to the author.

The Mould Numbers

THE MOULD NUMBERS BELOW ARE FROM THE SHAW AND COPESTAKE FACTORY AND SHOULD NOT CONTAIN ANY FALCON WARE NUMBERS. FALCON WARE NUMBERS are PREFIXED WITH 'F' AND ARE UNRELATED
See back page for further reading.

Price Guide

The task of assessing prices is a difficult one and it must be borne in mind that these are bound to vary since so much depends on prevailing market conditions.

The price for each pattern and / or shape may vary considerably depending on colour and condition.

In addition, it should be noted that the following decorations could be more than the values quoted, although every effort has been made to take account of them.

MATT DARK BLUE
PINK
HAND PAINTED; CELLULOSE OR GLOSS
SPECIAL DECORATIVE EFFECTS SUCH AS MARBLING OR DRIP GLAZE

As a general rule high glaze animals tend to fetch less than matt finish, except in certain lines.

Acknowledgements

Once again, my thanks go to the many collectors who have shared SylvaC information with me. In particular, I gratefully acknowledge the following: Mick and Derry Collins of The SylvaC Collectors Circle, Susan Verbeek, Mr Mrs Howe, N Rees and L Howe and specialist traders.

FACTORY MARKS FOR SYLVAC AND SHAW AND COPESTAKE

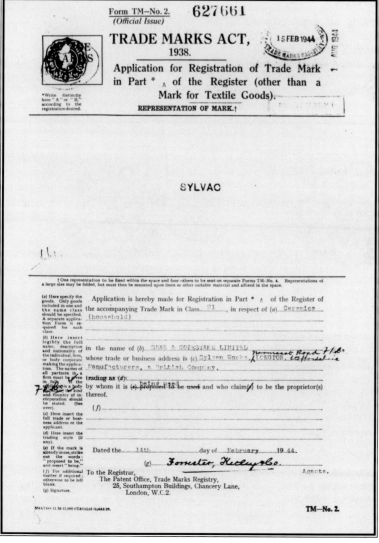

SylvaC copy Certificate application. The trade name was renewed on the 15th February 1951 and subsequently on the 15th February 1979 which remained in force until 15th February 1993.

The "Daisy" marks were used until the end of the 1930's. Gradually, as the patterns and wares changed, the "Daisy" was replaced by the name "SylvaC" which began to be impressed next to the mould numbers on the base of the newer novelties. Sometimes sticky "SylvaC" labels were also used when there was no other identification. Unfortunately these have a tendency to wash off. The "Daisy" mark was not used after the Second World War.

THE DAISY MARK

The standard mark is an eight petalled daisy and dots, with "Made in England" inside the circumference and a small daisy in the centre. The daisy occurs in three colours, green (possibly early), black (standard), and gold (used probably on prestige wares or those with considerable gold decoration).

It is rare to find the combined marks used on early cellulose, but it is seen with the "Semi-Porcelain" deleted.

Standard Daisy c. 1912-39

Small Daisy only 1912-39

Daisy with SylvaC and semi-porcelain known as the combined mark c. 1935-39

Daisy with SylvaC only c. 1935-37

IMPRESSED MARKS

Numbers, names and "Made in England" are found on the base of many wares, the mould numbers started around 1906.

Applied Registered design number and mould number 1913

Made in England with mould number c. 1928 onward.

Silvo early 1930's-1939

Napier mid 1920's-1939

Portland vase 1927-1936

Roman c. 1928-36

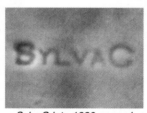

SylvaC late 1930 onward

Portland vase 1927-1936

Anomalies 338 mirrored numbers any date

LABELS *applied or painted*

"Scello" ware early name for cellulose products c. 1928-1935

Wild Duck c. 1931 onwards

Harvest Poppy c. 1932-1939 (Carnation not illustrated - 1934-1936)

Cornflower c. 1936-1939

Egyptian c. 1932-1936

SylvaC labels silver and black c. 1935/6 - c. 1940

SylvaC label black and white late 1930's-1940's plus

OTHER MARKS

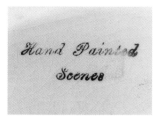

Hand Painted 1920's
and 1930's

Moonlight 1500 c. 1920's

Base showing decoration number
from c. 1919 onwards

1950s - 60s

1960s

1940 - 50

1960s - on

1950 - 60

1939 - 50

1970s - on

OTHER MARKS (contined)

Display 2

1945 - 55

1949

1960 - 70

1950s - on

1980

Display

1960s

SYLVAC MODERN REPRODUCTIONS AND COPIES

Here are two lists of items to watch out for Supplied by Kind permission of the SylvaC Collectors Club. (Address back Page)

1. These Items are **COPIES** of original SylvaC pieces but are all **SMALLER** than the originals and are produced in various colours and finishes

(F) denotes a Falcon ware factory number the others are Shaw and Copestake

	size of original is		size of original is
(F) 16 Bulldog 1380 Large Terrier	. . .6.25"h	1380 Large Terrier	. . . . .11"h
(F) 31 Dog and Slipper	. . . . .6"l	1433 Dog with Arm in Sling	. . . . .3.5"h
(F) 320 Pixies Wall Pocket	. . . . .7.5"h	1462 Spaniel	. . . . .11"h
919 Dancing Lady	. . . . .8.5"h	1499 Duck size 3	. . . . .4.25"h
990 Snub Nose Rabbit	. . . . .5"h	1543/5 Set of Seagulls	. . . . . . .4.5" & 8.5"h
1026 Snub Nose Rabbit	. . . . .6.75"h	1546 Bookend with Rabbits	. . . . .4.5"h
1027 Snub Nose Rabbit	. . . . .8.25"h	1548 Collie	. . . . .5.25"h
1028 Snub Nose Rabbit	. . . . .9.75"h	1959 Squirrel and Acorn Jug	. . . . .8.5"h
1046 Frightened Cat	. . . . .6"h	1960 Stork Jug	. . . . .10"h
1119 Daisy Dog	. . . . .4"h	1969 Gnome and Mushroom Jug	. . . . .8.5"h
1208 Mac Dog	. . . . .9"h	3294 Jug with embossed Squirrel (not original S&C)
1299 Hare	. . . . .7.75"h	3392 Caricature Long Neck Cat	. . . . . . .12.75"h
1304 Large Lop Eared Rabbit	. . . . . .8.5"h	3542 Mr SylvaC	. . . . .8"h
1318 Climbing Rabbits Jug	. . . . .8.75"h	5111 Cat	. . . . .8.75"h
1382 Spaniel	. . . . .8"h		

2. The following are sometimes found as **MODERN REPRODUCTIONS** legitimately produced with the original moulds. These pieces are usually found in either fawn or green but other finishes have been used. Because these items are produced from the original moulds they often carry the same SylvaC name and number. **When buying any of these be sure of their provenance and always buy from a reputable dealer.**

(F)18 Spaniel sitting
1043 Bulldog with Bow
1207 'Mac' Dog size 3
1378 Terrier
1509 Lop eared Rabbit size 1
2451 Toothache Dog size 4
2455 Toothache Dog size 3
2693 Tennis Player dog jug (very few if any made)
2807 Min Monkey & Coconut Jug
2938/50/51 Hang Dogs
3133 Corgi Pup sitting
3275 Spaniel with Pipe in Mouth
3459 Otter Prestige range
3827 Spaniel holding slipper
3930 Bull Prestige range
5023 Shetland Sheepdog (not produced in matt glaze originally)
(F)455 Dovecote Jug

5027 Yorkshire Terrier(not produced in matt glaze originally)
5031 Poodle(not produced in matt glaze originally)
5194 Doggy's dinner pot
5289/90/91 Rabbits(thumper)
5292/93/94 Dogs (Long Neck)
5301/02/03 Ugly Sheepdogs
5314 Alice with Goat
5315 Adam The Game Keeper
5316 Katie the Goose Girl
5548/49/50 Nosy Parker Cruet(Usually no Lid to Vinegar)
5661 Basset Hound Money Box(never produced in fawn or green)
Facepots Various- Horseradish, Tartare, Coleslaw,Onion Cucumber,Chutney,Pickled Cabbage,Parsley,

Mould No	Description	Size	Price Guide in £'s	Colour	Date Purchased	Price Paid
1.	N/I					
2.	Vase tall 2 handles		40-60			
3-15	N/I					
16.	Vase		30-45			
17-18	N/I					
19.	Jug Narrow neck		25-35			
20-29	N/I					
30.	Vase Narrow neck		25-35			
31-35	N/I					
36.	Jug	16"h	40-60			
37-74	N/I					
75.	Vase	9"h	25-35			
76-84	N/I					
85.	Vase		20-30			
86-124	N/I					
125.	Plant pot similar to 127 & 404		25-35			
126.	N/I					
127.	Plant pot similar to 125 & 404	7"h 9"dia	40-70			
128-137	N/I					
138.	Vase	10.75"h	25-60			
139.	Vase	11"h	25-60			
140-156	N/I					
157.	Jardiniere		30-40			

Mould No	Description	Size	Price Guide in £'s	Colour	Date Purchased	Price Paid
158-169	N/I					
170	Vase		20-45			
171-175	N/I					
176.	Clock with pillars	16"h	40-80			
177.	N/I					
178.	Vase For spills	4.5"h	15-25			
179-182	N/I					
183.	Plant pot		35-45			
184.	N/I					
185.	Jardiniere	5"h 4.75"dia	25-45			
186-195	N/I					
196.	Vase similar to 496		25-50			
197-229	N/I					
230.	Clock	11.5"h 9"w	40-80			
231-254.	N/I					
255.	Vase	13.75"h	20-50			
256-261.	N/I					
262.	Plant pot	6.5"h 6.75"dia	45-60			
263-269	N/I					
270.	Vase		20-35			
271.	N/I					
272.	N/I					
273.	Vase	9.25"h	25-40			

Mould No	Description	Size	Price Guide in £'s	Colour	Date Purchased	Price Paid
274-278	N/I					
279.	Vase Reg No 628381 year 1913	11.75"h	30-50			
280.	N/I					
281.	Vase similar to 273	11.5"h	30-50			
282.	N/I					
283.	Plant pot		20-60			
284-291	N/I					
292.	Vase Reg No 633217	9.5"h	25-45			
293.	Vase Reg No 634174 year 1914	11.5"h	30-50			
294-301	N/I					
302.	Jardiniere	8"h 10"dia	40-60			
303.	Jardiniere	8.5"dia	25-50			
304-309	N/I					
310.	Vase		15-30			
311-314	N/I					
315.	Plant pot	6"h 5.25"dia	20-40			
316-320	N/I					
321.	Vase	9.5"h	25-45			
322-334	N/I					
335.	Vase	10"h	25-45			
336.	Vase similar to 335	7.5"h	20-35			
337.	Vase	12"h	20-50			
338.	Vase	13.25"h	25-50			

Mould No	Description	Size	Price Guide in £'s	Colour	Date Purchased	Price Paid
339.	N/I					
340.	Plant pot similar to 341		15-20			
341.	Jardiniere	6.5"h 6"dia	15-25			
342.	3 piece vase garniture set like 335	6"h and 7"h	25-50			
343-344	N/I					
345.	Plant pot 2 handles, 3 feet	4" dia	15-25			
346.	N/I					
347.	Vase	9.5"h	20-40			
348-349	N/I					
350.	Jardiniere on four feet scalloped top	5"h	20-40			
351.	Clock		40-75			
352.	Jardiniere as 350 & 357		15-25			
353.	N/I					
354.	Vase 'Holborn' reissued	16"h	100-150			
355.	Vase similar to 359	6.5"h	20-30			
356.	N/I					
357.	Jardiniere	4.5"h 4.5"dia	25-35			
358.	N/I					
359.	Vase Similar to 360	9.75"h	20-30			
360.	Vase Similar to 359	12"h	25-50			
361.	N/I					
362.	Plant pot	4.5"h 4.25"dia	25-35			
363.	Vase similar to 364 & 365	7.25"h	20-35			

Mould No	Description	Size	Price Guide in £'s	Colour	Date Purchased	Price Paid
364.	Vase similar to 363 & 365	9.5"h	30-45			
365.	Vase Similar to 363 & 364	11.75"h	35-50			
366.	Vase similar to 365	12"h	35-50			
367.	Vase	10"h	30-45			
368-370	N/I					
371.	Vase	10"h	30-45			
372-373	N/I					
374.	Vase	12"h	20-40			
375.	Tall vase	1.75"h	25-50			
376.	Vase oval centre to match 375	7"h 11.75"w	25-45			
377-378	N/I					
379.	Vase		20-35			
380.	Vase oval similar to 376	5"h 8"w	25-35			
381-386	N/I					
387.	Vase	11.5"h	35-55			
388-398	N/I					
399.	Jardiniere embossed shells as 401	4.5"h 4.5"dia	25-40			
400.	N/I					
401.	Jardiniere embossed shells as 399	6.25"h 6.25" dia	30-60			
402-403	N/I					
404.	Plant pot similar to 127	7"dia 7.25"h	30-45			
405-410	N/I					
411.	Jardiniere Similar to 125, 127 & 404	6.25"dia 5.25"h	30-60			

Mould No	Description	Size	Price Guide in £'s	Colour	Date Purchased	Price Paid
412.	Bowl	11.5"dia	30-45			
413.	N/I					
414.	N/I					
415.	Vase		20-40			
416.	Vase similar to 418	10"h	30-60			
417.	Vase octagonal similar to 421		15-25			
418.	Vase similar to 416	7.5"h	15-30			
419.	Vase similar to 425 & 445	11.75"h	25-55			
420.	Vase	11.5"h	25-55			
421.	Vase	7.5"h	20-35			
422.	Vase	8.5"h	15-30			
423.	N/I					
424.	Vase similar to 540		20-30			
425.	Vase similar to 419 & 445	9.5"h	20-35			
426.	Vase	8.25"h	20-35			
427-430	N/I					
428	Rose bowl	11.5"h	35-55			
431.	Vase similar to 432	8.25"h	15-35			
432.	Vase	7.5"h	15-35			
433.	Clock to go with vase 433	5"h	40-60			
433.	Vase to go with clock 433	4"h	10-20			
434.	Vase		10-20			
435.	N/I					

Mould No	Description	Size	Price Guide in £'s	Colour	Date Purchased	Price Paid
436.	Bowl melon shaped also used with centerpiece	9.5"dia 2.5"h	20-40			
437.	N/I					
438.	N/I					
439.	Vase	7.5"h	15-30			
440.	Centre piece.	7"h 6.5"dia	30-50			
441.	Rose bowl	4"h 6.5"dia	25-35			
442.	N/I					
443.	Vase	6"h	15-25			
444.	N/I					
445.	Vase	8.25"h	20-35			
446.	Vase similar to 421	8.5"h	20-40			
447.	Rose bowl		23-35			
448.	N/I					
449.	Vase	14"h	30-55			
450-464	N/I					
465.	Vase embossed	7.5"h	20-35			
466-476	N/I					
477.	Flower Holder	3"h 7.5"l	15-25			
478-481	N/I					
482.	Clock	12"h	40-80			
483.	Vase for spills	4.75"h	15-25			
484.	Shaving mug	4.25"h	25-60			
485-488	N/I					

Mould No	Description	Size	Price Guide in £'s	Colour	Date Purchased	Price Paid
489.	Hexagonal bowl	7.75"dia	20-60			
490.	N/I					
491.	N/I					
492.	Rose bowl	5.75"h 4.5"w	15-40			
493.	Shaving mug	4"h	25-40			
494.	N/I					
495.	Vase similar to 510	11.5"h	30-60			
496.	Vase Similar to 196	11"h	30-60			
497-508	N/I					
509.	Vase similar to 496	10"h	30-55			
510.	Clock small		40-60			
510.	Vase similar to 495	9.5"h	20-45			
511.	Vase to go with clock 520	11.5"h	30-60			
512-519	N/I					
520.	Clock	14"h 10.5"w	45-80			
521.	Vase	12"h	35-55			
522.	Vase	13.75"h	40-60			
522.	Plinth round	7.25"dia	10-15			
523.	Dressing table tray octagonal	13.5"l	25-45			
524-527	N/I					
528.	Vase	13"h	40-60			
529-532	N/I					
533.	Vase for spills	7"h	20-35			

Mould No	Description	Size	Price Guide in £'s	Colour	Date Purchased	Price Paid
534.	Vase for spills	8"h	20-40			
535.	N/I					
536.	N/I					
537.	N/I					
538.	Vase similar to 539/40/41/58/62	7.75"h	20-40			
539.	Vase similar to 538/40/41/58/62	8.5"h	25-50			
540.	Vase similar to 538/39/41/58/62	8"h	20-40			
541.	Vase similar to 538/39/40/58/62	11.5"h	30-60			
542.	Tray 'Napier'		25-40			
543.	Vase for spills	6"h	15-25			
544.	N/I					
545.	Vase	6"h	10-20			
546.	Vase similar to 548	8.5"h	20-40			
547.	N/I					
548.	Vase similar to 546, with of without lid	11.25"h	40-80			
548.	Vase similar to 546 with a lid	17"h	40-70			
549-552	N/I					
553.	Rose bowl similar to 559		15-30			
554-555	N/I					
556.	Vase similar to 634,636		15-30			
557.	Bowl wavy edges	3"h	10-20			
558.	Vase similar to 538/39/40/62		20-50			
559.	Rose bowl similar to 553 not embossed	6.5" dia 4.5"h	15-35			

Mould No	Description	Size	Price Guide in £'s	Colour	Date Purchased	Price Paid
559.	Rose bowl embossed 'Wild Duck' ware	6.5" dia 4.5"h	15-35			
560.	Jug	8.5"h	20-45			
561.	Vase	7.5"h	20-35			
562.	Vase similar to 538/39/40/41/58	14"h	30-60			
563.	Jug	6.75"h - 7.75"h	20-45			
564.	Vase	12"h	35-60			
565.	Vase	11.5"h	30-60			
566.	Rose bowl	5"dia	20-40			
567.	Vase	11.5"h	30-60			
568.	N/I					
569.	Bowl 'Wild Duck' ware		20-35			
570.	Vase	8.25"h	15-25			
571.	N/I					
572.	N/I					
573.	Jugs sizes 1-5.	7.75"h - 5.25"h	15-40			
574.	Figure 'Tiki' A commission for the family	6"-7"h	60-100			
575.	Rose bowl two handles	8.5"h	35-60			
576.	Vase	11"h	30-60			
577.	Vase		15-30			
578.	Vase	6.75"h	15-25			
579.	N/I					
580.	Plant pot on four feet	4"h	15-30			
581.	Vase similar to 582/3	9.75"h	20-40			

Mould No	Description	Size	Price Guide in £'s	Colour	Date Purchased	Price Paid
582.	Vase similar to 581 583	11.5"h	40-55			
583.	Vase similar to 581 582	13.75"h	45-60			
584.	N/I					
585.	Vase		20-40			
586.	N/I					
587.	Vase	9.5"h	20-40			
588-593	N/I					
594.	Tray 'Sylvo'	13.5"l 6"w	20-40			
595-598	N/I					
599.	Rose bowl similar to 566		25-40			
600.	Vase similar to 610,611	9.5"h	20-40			
601.	Flower pot	5"dia	25-40			
602.	Jardiniere similar to 603	5"h 6"dia	20-40			
603.	Plant pot similar to 602	6"h 7"dia	20-40			
604.	Clock	12"h	50-85			
605.	Heart shape clock to go with 606	9.75"h	45-80			
606.	Heart shape vase to go with 605	7.5"h	20-35			
607.	Bowl for baby With alphabet	7"dia	60-80			
608.	Heart shape clock circular or square centres	11.75"h	50-80			
609.	Heart shape vase to go with 608	9.75"h	20-35			
610.	Vase similar to 600, 611	8.5"h	20-35			
611.	Vase	11.75"h	25-45			
612.	N/I					

Mould No	Description	Size	Price Guide in £'s	Colour	Date Purchased	Price Paid
613.	Vase	8"h	20-30			
614.	Vase	9.75"h	20-40			
615-619	N/I					
620.	Tray dressing table		20-40			
620.	Flower pot	6.25"h	25-40			
621.	Vase tall shaped	13.5"h	25-50			
622.	Vase Similar to 627,626	14"h	40-65			
624.	Hat pin holder	3.5"h	15-25			
623-625	N/I					
626.	Vase similar to 627,622	7.75"h	15-35			
627.	Vase similar to 626,622	10"h	25-45			
628.	N/I					
629.	Vase	11.5"h	30-50			
630.	Clock	14"h	40-80			
631.	Bowl round on three legs	7"dia	30-50			
632.	Biscuit Barrel	5.5"h	30-50			
633.	N/I					
634.	Vase for spills	6"h	15-25			
635.	Vase for spills seen with silver rim		25-45			
636.	Vase for spill similar to 634 large	8"h	20-30			
637.	Vase	12"h	25-50			
638-639	N/I					
640.	Tray		20-30			

Mould No	Description	Size	Price Guide in £'s	Colour	Date Purchased	Price Paid
641.	N/I					
642.	Shaving mug	3.24"h	30-50			
643.	Cheese dish	7.5"l	30-50			
644.	N/I					
645.	Clock	11.5"h	40-80			
646.	N/I					
647.	N/I					
648.	Gothic style clock to go with vase	11.5"h	40-80			
648.	Gothic style vase to go with clock	10.5"h	30-45			
649.	Clock not embossed with vase 650	10"h	40-70			
649.	Clock embossed 'Wild Duck' ware	10"h	25-45			
650.	Vase to go with clock 649	7.5"h	25-35			
650.	Vase embossed 'Wild Duck' ware	7.5"h	15-25			
651.	Clock to go with vase 652	8.75"h x 11.25"w	45-85			
652.	Vase to clock 651	8.5"h	25-50			
653.	Vase with silver rim	5"h	25-45			
654.	Sandwich tray	12.5"l	20-40			
	+ plates not numbered to match above tray	each	10-15			
655-658	N/I					
659.	'Scello' ware vase	9.5"h	15-30			
660-662	N/I					
663.	Embossed Chinese ladies like 703	12"h	25-45			
664.	N/I					

Mould No	Description	Size	Price Guide in £'s	Colour	Date Purchased	Price Paid
665.	N/I					
666.	Octagonal jug at least 3 sizes	6"+7"+ 8" h	15-40			
667-668	N/I					
669.	Vase similar to 696	11"h	25-40			
670-673	N/I					
674.	Plate oval		15-35			
675.	Wall plate	11.75"l 8"w	50-70			
676-677	N/I					
678.	Vase similar to 679	10"h	20-40			
679.	Vase similar to 678	11"h	25-45			
680.	Bowl with bird Falcon, kingfisher	8.5"dia	20-45			
681.	N/I					
682.	Clock similar to 783	12"h	50-80			
683.	Butter/Cheese dish	3"h	20-35			
684.	Vase	6"h	15-30			
685-688	N/I					
689.	Plant pot embossed, Lord and Lady in Garden	4.5"h	15-25			
690.	Plant pot embossed, Lord and Lady in Garden	5.5"h	15-25			
691.	N/I					
692.	N/I					
693.	Plant pot embossed, large Lord and Lady in Garden		25-35			
694.	Clock set (clock and vases) Lord and Lady in Garden		40-60			
694.	Dish hexagonal	5"w	15-25			

Mould No	Description	Size	Price Guide in £'s	Colour	Date Purchased	Price Paid
695.	Clock set 3pce similar to 696		65-120			
696.	3pce clock set Lord & Lady		65-120			
696.	Clock	9.75"h x 7.75"w	40-60			
696.	Vase to go with clock above	8.5"h x 4"w	15-25			
697.	Vase Lord and Lady similar to 699 embossed	7.75h	15-30			
698.	Vase Lord and Lady	9.75"h	20-40			
699.	Vase Lord and Lady similar to 697	11.5"h	20-40			
700.	Kingfisher bird to go in bowl often No 436	6.5"h	30-60			
701.	Swallow centre piece?					
702.	N/I					
703.	Vase embossed Chinese ladies like 663	10"h	20-40			
704.	Pot embossed Lord and Lady scene	4.75"h	15-25			
705.	Pot as 704	9.75"h	15-35			
706-708						
709.	Vase Spanish couple on balcony	10"h	20-40			
710.	N/I					
711.	Bowl embossed marigold	11.25"d 3"h	15-25			
712-713	N/I					
714.	Plant pot Lord and Lady similar to 704	6"dia	15-30			
715.	Plant pot Lord and Lady similar to 704	8.5"dia	20-40			
716.	Jardiniere embossed Lord and lady	11"dia	20-35			
717.	N/I					
718.	Plant pot Lord and Lady in Garden	6.25"dia	15-30			

Mould No	Description	Size	Price Guide in £'s	Colour	Date Purchased	Price Paid
719.	N/I					
720.	N/I					
721.	N/I					
722.	Bowl embossed octagonal fairy scene	11"dia	15-25			
723.	N/I					
724.	N/I					
725.	N/I					
726.	Bowl embossed garden scene	9.5"dia 2.5"h	15-25			
727.	Double Vase Sydney Harbour Bridge	8.5"l 4.5"h	60-80			
728.	Rose bowl embossed Lord and Lady	6"h	15-35			
729-732	N/I					
733.	Pelican with top hat & rock vase	8"h	80-120			
734-742	N/I					
743.	Airedale Terrier with vase 827 attached	7"h 9"l	60-100			
744.	Clock	10.5"h 10.5"w	40-80			
745.	N/I					
746.	N/I					
747.	Bowl with monkey in centre	7"dia	80-100			
748.	N/I					
749.	Vase	6"h	15-25			
750.	N/I					
751.	Dog		35-60			
752.	Pekinese	6.5"h 7.5"l	60-100			

Mould No	Description	Size	Price Guide in £'s	Colour	Date Purchased	Price Paid
753.	Plant pot embossed cottage similar to 2690 2691	6"dia	25-35			
754.	Bowl	9"dia				
755-756	N/I					
757.	Plant holder 'Wild Duck' ware Reg No 762858	large	20-35			
758.	Plant pot 'Wild Duck' ware Similar to 757,812	10.5"dia	20-35			
759.	Jardiniere shell		20-30			
760.	N/I					
761.	N/I					
762.	Clock Owl	10"h	60-75			
763.	Vase Owl	8.5"h	30-55			
764.	N/I					
765.	Swan		15-30			
766.	Camel with saddlebags	5.5"h	30-45			
767.	Camel with saddlebags on plinth	5.5"l 4.25"h	30-45			
768.	Standing elephant	4"h	15-45			
769.	Standing elephant	6"h	20-60			
770.	Standing elephant	7.25"h	25-70			
771.	Standing elephant also seen on base	8.5"h	35-85			
772.	Camel standing with howdah	9" x 7"h	40-70			
773.	Elephant with howdah	8.5"h	45-60			
774.	Vase	12"h	30-50			
775.	N/I					
776.	Vase fan shape embossed with roses	8"w	15-25			

Mould No	Description	Size	Price Guide in £'s	Colour	Date Purchased	Price Paid
777.	N/I					
778.	Vase similar to 776	10.25"w	15-30			
779.	Cheetah		60-95			
780.	Vase	5"h	10-15			
781.	Vase spill	4.5"h	10-15			
782.	Vase embossed Lord and Lady		15-25			
783.	Clock Similar to 682	10"h 14.5"w	50-70			
784.	Vase embossed 'Wild Duck' ware	7.75"h	20-30			
785.	Vase embossed 'Wild Duck' ware	5.25"h	15-25			
786.	Bowl embossed 'Wild Duck' ware square	9"sq	30-45			
787.	Flying duck flower stand goes with 786	7.5"h	50-70			
788.	Elephant with howdah	6"h	30-45			
789.	Elephant with howdah	7"h	30-45			
790.	Vase 'Wild Duck' ware Reg No. 768168	5.75"h 8.25"w	15-25			
791.	Vase 'Wild Duck' ware	7"h	20-30			
792.	Plant pot 'Wild Duck' ware	9"dia	20-35			
793.	Swan	5.25"h 7.5"l	25-35			
794.	Swan S/S		15-30			
795.	Swan L/S	7.5"h 10"l	50-80			
796.	N/I					
797.	N/I					
798.	Elephant with howdah	L/S	40-70			
799.	Vase 'Wild Duck' ware Reg No 768695	9"h	20-35			

Mould No	Description	Size	Price Guide in £'s	Colour	Date Purchased	Price Paid
800.	N/I					
801.	Vase embossed 'Wild Duck' ware Reg No 768695	10"h	25-35			
802.	Tray for dressing table 'Wild Duck' ware	16.75"l	25-45			
803.	Candlestick 'Wild Duck' ware Reg No 769028	6"h	10-20			
804.	Box 'Wild Duck' ware Reg No 769029	3"h	15-35			
805.	Box 'Wild Duck' ware Reg No as 804	2.5"h 6.5"l	15-30			
806.	Clock Set		100-150			
807.	N/I					
808.	N/I					
809.	Oval vase 'Wild Duck' ware Reg No 769285	5.5"h	15-30			
810.	N/I					
811.	Toilet set jug 'Wild Duck' ware Reg No 769699	10"h	40-60			
811.	Toilet set bowl 'Wild Duck' ware Reg No 769725	18"dia	30-40			
812.	Plant pot 'Wild Duck' ware Reg No 762858	7"dia	15-25			
813.	Toby jug 'Sam Weller' similar to 1231	8.5"h	60-100			
814.	Elephant with howdah	4.25"l 4"h	20-30			
815.	Elephant	4.5"h	15-25			
816.	Elephant		15-25			
817.	Lion	4.75"h	40-50			
818.	Lion	6"l 4"h	45-65			
819.	Lion large as on 822	12"l 6.75"h	80-100			
820.	Lion on plinth	8.5"l	60-80			
821.	Lion on plinth	10.25"l	70-90			

Mould No	Description	Size	Price Guide in £'s	Colour	Date Purchased	Price Paid
822.	Lion on plinth also as table lamp	11.5"l 7.75"h	60-110			
823.	Lion plinth and tree stump vase to go with 824	9.5"l 5.5"h	40-80			
824.	Lion plinth and tree stump vase to go with 823	9.5"l 5.5"h	40-80			
825.	Lion on plinth with vase	11"l 7.75"h	80-110			
826.	Elephant with howdah	4.5"h	25-30			
827.	Vase with Airedale dog attached	4.25"h	50-80			
828.	Vase ribbed Greek urn shape	8.5"h	20-30			
829.	Jug 'Egyptian' ware Reg No 774557	7.75"h	40-70			
830.	N/I					
831.	Rectangular Bowl 'Egyptian' ware Reg No 774557		20-35			
832.	Vase 'Egyptian' ware Reg No 774557	7.25"h	20-35			
833.	Vase 'Egyptian' ware Reg No 774557	8.75"h	20-35			
834.	Plant pot 'Egyptian' range	6"h	20-30			
835.	Jardiniere 'Egyptian' ware Reg No 774557	7.75"h	20-35			
836.	N/I					
837.	Rose bowl 'Egyptian' ware Reg No 774557	6"dia 4.5"h	15-25			
838.	Vase 'Egyptian' ware Reg No 774557	7"h	25-40			
839.	Vase 'Egyptian' ware Reg No 774557	7.5"h	25-35			
840.	Portland Vase 'Egyptian' ware Reg No 774557	8.25"h	30-55			
841.	Vase stand 'Egyptian' ware to fit 838		3-6			
842.	Goblin 'Billikens' long tongue and five toes	5.75"h	55-90			
843.	Laughing cat with bow tie	8.5"h	80-105			
844.	Laughing cat with vase & separate head	8.5"h	80-110			

Mould No	Description	Size	Price Guide in £'s	Colour	Date Purchased	Price Paid
845.	Goblin 'Billikens' with vase similar to 842	7.25"h	50-80			
846.	Panther with howdah	6"h	60-95			
847.	Figurine vase 'Covent Garden' flower girl	10"h	50-90			
848.	Vase oval 'Harvest Poppy' ware	10.5"l x 5.75"h	15-35			
849.	Cheese dish decorated "From Southsea"	5.25"l	20-35			
850.	Bird on tree stump	7.5"h	40-60			
851-855	N/I					
856.	Vase 'Egyptian' ware similar to 832	7"h	25-35			
857.	Rose bowl vase tree trunk		20-30			
858.	Tree trunk vase for roses embossed with flowers	5"h	15-25			
859.	N/I					
860.	N/I					
861.	Vase	7.75"h	20-40			
862.	Clock 'Egyptian' ware with 832, Reg No 774557	9"h 7"w	50-80			
863.	Bowl 'Egyptian' ware		15-25			
864.	Sphinx on pedestal	6"h	40-60			
865.	Figurine vase Covent Garden flower seller	10"h	75-90			
865.	Plant pot Egyptian		25-35			
866-872	N/I					
873.	Vase embossed 'Story time'	12"h	25-40			
874.	Vase 'Egyptian' range	7.75"h	25-35			
875.	Bowl hexagonal 'Story book'	10"w	15-20			
876-879	N/I					

Mould No	Description	Size	Price Guide in £'s	Colour	Date Purchased	Price Paid
880.	Figurine lady holding 30'S dress	8.5"h	60-110			
881.	Figurine Spanish lady	9.5"h	60-110			
882.	Vase		15-30			
883.	Vase		15-30			
884.	Vase		15-30			
885.	Plant pot 'Egyptian' range		20-40			
886.	Jug size 1	8"h	25-45			
887.	Lady figurine in large dress curtsying	5"h	60-110			
888.	Lady figurine in feathered hat and muff	6.5"h	60-150			
889.	Lady figurine in skirt shawl and bonnet	7.25"h	60-110			
890.	Lady figurine in skirt and bunch of flowers		60-110			
891.	Dutch clog		15-20			
892.	Plant pot	6"h	20-35			
893.	Jardiniere	6.75"h 4.25"dia	25-40			
894.	Jardiniere Similar to 893	8.5"h	30-45			
895.	Vase 'Egyptian' ware Reg No 774557		20-35			
896.	N/I					
897.	N/I					
898.	Vase diamond shape 10"l Deco sun ray	5.5"h	30-50			
899.	N/I					
900.	N/I					
901.	N/I					
902.	Ginger jar shape similar to 903	7.25"h	30-45			

Mould No	Description	Size	Price Guide in £'s	Colour	Date Purchased	Price Paid
903.	Ginger jar as 902 'Harvest Poppy' ware	8.25"h	35-50			
904.	Vase 'Harvest Poppy' ware	7.25"h	20-35			
905.	Vase diamond shape 'Harvest Poppy' ware	8.75"h	15-25			
906.	N/I					
907.	Vase	5"h	15-25			
908.	Vase 'Harvest Poppy' ware	7.5"h	20-35			
909.	N/I					
910.	Vase 'Harvest Poppy' ware	9"h	25-45			
911-914	N/I					
915.	Plant pot 'Harvest Poppy' ware	8"h	20-45			
916.	N/I					
917.	Jug 'Harvest Poppy' ware	8"h	20-40			
918.	Rose Bowl 'Harvest Poppy' ware	5.5"h	15-25			
919.	Lady figurine ruffled sleeves holding skirt	8.5"h	50-180			
920.	Lady figurine holding out skirts	8.5"h	80-130			
921-925	N/I					
926.	Plant pot 'Egyptian' ware Reg No 774557	4.24"h 4".75w	20-30			
927.	Vase fan shape 'Cornflower' ware		10-20			
928.	N/I					
929.	N/I					
930.	Pierrette figurine to go with 931	8.75"h	120-180			
931.	Pierrot figurine to go with 930	8.75"h	120-180			
932.	N/I					

Mould No	Description	Size	Price Guide in £'s	Colour	Date Purchased	Price Paid
933.	N/I					
934.	N/I					
935.	Jug Embossed leaves and fruit		15-25			
936.	Vase 'Palestine' ware	9"h	30-45			
937.	Bowl 'Palestine' ware		30-45			
938.	Rose bowl 'Palestine' ware		15-35			
939.	N/I					
940.	Plant pot 'Palestine' ware	7"dia	20-45			
941.	N/I					
942.	Vase 'Palestine' ware	8.5"h	25-40			
943.	Bowl 'Palestine' ware Embossed Arab scene	11"dia	25-55			
944.	Beaker/Vase 'Palestine' ware	6"h	20-40			
945.	Pot & lid 'Palestine' ware	5.25"h 5.5"dia	30-50			
946.	N/I					
947.	N/I					
948.	Pastille burner 'Palestine' ware	9"h	35-65			
949-953	N/I					
954.	Jug		15-30			
955.	Bowl		20-30			
956.	Jug		15-30			
957.	Vase Poppy flower on stem		15-25			
958.	Rose bowl Embossed 'Cornflower' ware	6"h	15-25			
959.	N/I					

Mould No	Description	Size	Price Guide in £'s	Colour	Date Purchased	Price Paid
960.	N/I					
961.	Shoe	5"l	10-15			
962.	Gnome standing	5"h	50-80			
963.	N/I					
964.	Jug embossed 'Cornflower' ware	7.5"h	20-30			
965.	Rose bowl 'Cornflower' ware		15-25			
966.	Vase embossed 'Cornflower' ware	6" h	15-25			
967.	Vase embossed 'Cornflower' ware	8.5"h	20-30			
968.	N/I					
969.	N/I					
970.	Bowl 'Cornflower' ware	6"h	20-30			
971.	Jardiniere 'Cornflower' ware	6.5"h	30-40			
972.	N/I					
973.	Posy vase with rabbits		50-60			
974.	Vase oval 'Cornflower' ware		20-35			
975.	Vase	7.25"h	15-30			
976.	Vase 'Cornflower' ware		15-25			
977.	Vase 'Cornflower' ware		20-35			
978.	Vase 'Cornflower' ware	5.5"h	20-30			
979.	Vase 'Cornflower' ware	8"h	20-35			
980.	N/I					
981.	Cat sitting up	6.75"h	60-80			
982.	Cat similar to 981	8"h	70-90			

Mould No	Description	Size	Price Guide in £'s	Colour	Date Purchased	Price Paid
983.	Basket with ceramic grid		25-50			
984.	Three monkeys Hear/speak/see no evil	2.25"h	40-60			
985.	Plant pot		15-25			
986.	N/I					
987.	Vase Embossed 'Cornflower' ware	11"h	20-30			
988.	N/I					
989.	Footballer Reg No 787779 (1933)	8"h	175-250			
990.	Bunny snub nose	5"h	50-95			
991.	Lion	7.25"l 3.75"h	40-50			
992.	Puss in shoe	5"l 4"h	30-50			
993.	Fortune teller	3.75"h	70-90			
994-999	N/I					
1000.	Jug sim to 1253		25-45			
1001.	Jug ribbed	7"h	25-45			
1002.	Vase	8.5"h	25-35			
1003.	Posy holder round		5-15			
1004.	Owl and tree trunk vase	6.5"h	50-70			
1005.	Vase spill	6"h	15-25			
1006.	Vase with handles	8.5"h	25-45			
1007.	Vase sim to 1008	5"h	15-25			
1008.	Vase sim to 1007	8"h	20-30			
1009.	N/I					
1010.	N/I					

Mould No	Description	Size	Price Guide in £'s	Colour	Date Purchased	Price Paid
1011.	Vase	8.25"h	20-35			
1012.	Jug	6"h	20-30			
1013.	Vase bulbous	7"h	15-25			
1014.	Vase bulbous	8.5"h	15-30			
1015.	N/I					
1016.	N/I					
1017.	Vase	8.25"h	25-45			
1018.	Cat scared		40-50			
1019.	Plant pot similar to 603		25-45			
1020.	N/I					
1021.	Pixie sitting under mushroom	3.5"h	100-120			
1022.	Figure of black boy with banjo	5"h	120-175			
1023.	Boy soldier	5.5"h	120-175			
1024.	Gnome hugging his knees	4.5"h	40-90			
1025.	Vase deco angular 'Odeon' style	7"h	30-60			
1026.	Bunny	6.75"h	80-120			
1027.	Bunny	8.25"h	80-150			
1028.	Bunny	9.75"h	200-250			
1029-1031	N/I					
1032.	Vase	7"h	10-20			
1033.	Indian Chief on rock	7.25"h	200-250			
1034.	N/I					
1035.	Lady sitting with jug and mug in hand		60-120			

Mould No	Description	Size	Price Guide in £'s	Colour	Date Purchased	Price Paid
1036.	Red Ridinghood as 1081		75-120			
1037.	Donkey with baskets and girl on plinth	7"h 8"l	40-80			
1038.	Bulldog sitting	3"h	20-35			
1039.	Kingfisher vase	6" h	35-55			
1040.	Vase		10-20			
1041.	N/I					
1042.	Donkey with baskets and boy on plinth	7"h	40-80			
1043.	Bulldog with bow	7.5"h	70-100			
1044.	Bulldog with bow	8.5"h	90-120			
1045.	Bulldog with bow	10.5"h	100-175			
1046.	Cat standing, scared as 1313	6"h	30-50			
1047-1056	N/I					
1057.	Rabbit small		20-40			
1058-1060	N/I					
1061.	Vase		10-30			
1062.	N/I					
1063.	N/I					
1064.	Bunny with posy holder/striker	4.25"h	45-70			
1065.	Bunny	6"h	60-90			
1066.	Rabbit With vase on back	8.25"h	90-120			
1067.	Bunny	4"h	35-60			
1068.	Flower centre for bowl similar to 1069	10.5"h	25-35			
1069.	Bowl embossed flowers like 1075		20-40			

Mould No	Description	Size	Price Guide in £'s	Colour	Date Purchased	Price Paid
1070.	Flower jug ribbed similar to 1071	10.5"h	50-70			
1071.	Flower jug ribbed similar to 1070	7"h	20-30			
1072.	N/I					
1073.	N/I					
1074.	N/I					
1075.	Vase embossed flowers similar to 1077	6.5"h	20-40			
1076.	Vase square base similar to 1075	7.5"h	20-40			
1077.	Vase embossed flowers similar to 1075	8.75"h	25-45			
1078.	Jug embossed flowers	7"h	25-45			
1079.	Jug similar to 1078	10.5"h	50-60			
1080.	Figurine lady	5"h	70-120			
1081.	Figurine 'Red Ridinghood'	5"h	70-120			
1082.	Penguin	6.5"h	60-95			
1083.	N/I					
1084.	N/I					
1085.	N/I					
1086.	Cat sitting	5"h	15-40			
1087.	Cat sitting	7"h	15-45			
1088.	Cat sitting	9"h	30-60			
1089.	N/I					
1090.	Mug to match 1091	3.5"h	8-10			
1090.	Mug also commemorative	3.5"h	10-20			
1091.	Cider jug ribbed design		25-35			

Mould No	Description	Size	Price Guide in £'s	Colour	Date Purchased	Price Paid
1092.	Gnome standing holding his sides	8.25"h	70-100			
1093.	Gnome standing as 1092	9.5"h	90-120			
1094.	Gnome standing as 1092 & 1093	14"h	150-210			
1095.	Gnome with pot	8.25"h	80-100			
1096.	N/I					
1097.	Gnome with pot	9.5"h	90-120			
1098.	N/I					
1099.	Cat and basket		40-60			
1100.	Pig sitting similar to 1486	10"l	75-95			
1101-1107	N/I					
1108.	Jug deco	8"h	20-35			
1109.	Vase deco sun ray as 1384	7"h	30-50			
1110.	Vase flower holder 'Bacchanti' range	7"h	20-35			
1111.	Plant pot on three feet 'Bacchanti' range		30-45			
1112.	Flower jug 'Bacchanti' range	8"h	30-50			
1113.	Oval vase 'Bacchanti' range	10.5"w 5.75"h	20-35			
1114.	Jug embossed hollyhocks, branch handle	7.75"h	40-65			
1115.	Flower jug acorn with squirrel handle	9"h	30-50			
1116.	Flower jug with dragon handle	8.75"h	40-65			
1117.	Dog sitting large head	7"h	70-150			
1118.	Dog sitting 'Monty the mongrel'	6.5"h	50-80			
1119.	Dog sitting with bow	4"h	25-40			
1120.	Dog sitting	3.75"h	35-60			

Mould No	Description	Size	Price Guide in £'s	Colour	Date Purchased	Price Paid
1121.	Dog Terrier standing	4.75"h 6.5"l	25-50			
1122.	Dog Sealyham standing	3.75"h 5.5"l	25-40			
1123.	Dog Scottie standing	3.5"h	60-100			
1124.	N/I					
1125.	Flower jug 'Bacchanti' range	7"h	35-60			
1126.	Vase 'Bacchanti' range	8.75"h	35-60			
1127.	Posy holder S/S swan	5.5"l	15-20			
1128-1131	N/I					
1132.	Pig solid		18-30			
1132.	Money box pig	4"l	18-30			
1133.	N/I					
1134.	Jug cauldron	2.5"h	8-10			
1135.	Pot cauldron	3.75"h	8-10			
1136.	Bowl		8-15			
1137.	N/I					
1138.	Flower jug with stork handle	10"h	50-85			
1139.	Flower jug diamond shape	8.5"h	30-50			
1140.	Bowl to go with 1134	2.5"h	8-10			
1141.	N/I					
1142.	Squirrel	5.25"h	40-50			
1143.	Squirrel	6.75"h	45-55			
1144.	Squirrel	7.75"h	50-80			
1145.	Squirrel with hole for wool	8 5"h	80-120			

41

Mould No	Description	Size	Price Guide in £'s	Colour	Date Purchased	Price Paid
1146.	Squirrel	9.75"h	120-180			
1147.	Jug art deco style	6"h	40-65			
1148.	Deco vase	7.5"h	30-70			
1149.	Vase	7.75"h	30-50			
1150.	Flower jug round ribbed	5.25"h	20-50			
1151.	N/I					
1152.	N/I					
1153.	Small elephant vase/holder	3"h	15-25			
1154.	Boy whistling		90-120			
1155.	N/I					
1156.	Boy Duck dressed goes with 1157	4.75"h	150-200			
1157.	Mrs. Duck in fancy dress	8"h	200-250			
1158.	Mr. Duck to match 1157	9"h	300-350			
1159.	Cat 'Corkscrew Tail' Reg No 806569	6.25"h	70-120			
1160.	N/I					
1161.	Girl Shy		80-110			
1162.	Cat 'Corkscrew Tail' Reg No 806569	3.75"h	60-90			
1163.	Cat 'Corkscrew Tail' as above	7.25"h	150-250			
1164.	Cat 'Corkscrew Tail' Reg No 806569	11"h	450-550			
1165.	Vase deco	16.5"h	30-50			
1166.	Vase	16.75"h	30-50			
1167.	Jug with stag handle	8.5"h	150-220			
1168.	Dish oval	11.5"x 7.5"x2"h	15-25			

Mould No	Description	Size	Price Guide in £'s	Colour	Date Purchased	Price Paid
1169.	"Lucky Pixie" large	5.75"h	60-70			
1170.	Girl with banjo to match 1022	5"h	110-175			
1171.	Windmill	5"h	50-70			
1172.	Mr. Pig in cap and clothes	6"h	150-200			
1173.	Vase deco ribbed	7"h	20-50			
1174.	Vase for flowers triangular0	10"h	20-3			
1175.	Jug/vase deco Pilgrim shape	6"h	15-35			
1176.	Vase ribbed as 1177 & 1201	7.5"h	15-25			
1177.	Vase ribbed	8.75"h	15-25			
1178.	Flower pot ribbed	7.75"dia	20-30			
1179.	Cockerel in waistcoat		80-150			
1180.	Chicken caricature		80-150			
1181.	Ashtray hare & holder No 1270	2.5"h	40-50			
1181.	Ashtray with rabbits		40-65			
1182.	Rabbit	2.5"h	30-45			
1183.	Cruet set ribbed	5"dia 2.5"h	35-45			
1184.	Honey pot ribbed	4.5"h	10-15			
1185.	Butter dish round ribbed	6"dia	15-25			
1186.	Posy bowl	8"dia	10-15			
1187.	Spill vase	4.25"h	10-18			
1188.	Dish ribbed	5.5"h	10-15			
1189.	Flower jug triangular shape	11.5"h	30-40			
1190.	Flower jug monkey nut Reg No 809067	7.25"h	65-175			

Mould No	Description	Size	Price Guide in £'s	Colour	Date Purchased	Price Paid
1191.	Dog sitting 'Joey' on collar	5"h	80-100			
1192.	Dog sitting 'Joey' on collar	6"h	100-125			
1193.	Dog sitting 'Joey' on collar	8"h	150-250			
1194.	Dog sitting 'Joey' on collar	9.5"h	275-375			
1195.	Flower jug acorn with squirrel handle	7.5"h	30-40			
1196.	Flower jug mushroom & gnomes Reg No 809115	8.5"h	35-60			
1197.	Cake stand		20-30			
1198.	Dish & stand oval watercress	11.25l 7"w	20-30			
1199.	Dish oval		10-20			
1200.	Rabbit		50-60			
1201.	Vase	5"h	8-10			
1202.	Dog Alsatian	7.25"h	80-120			
1203.	Alsatian dog sitting	9"h	150-200			
1204.	N/I					
1205.	Scottie dog Reg No 778504 Nov 1932	5"h	20-50			
1206.	Scottie dog Reg No 778504 Nov 1932	6.25"h	25-60			
1207.	Scottie dog Reg No 778504 Nov 1932	7.75"h	30-95			
1208.	Scottie dog Reg No 778504 Nov 1932	9"h	50-125			
1208.	Scottie dog as 1208 with golf ball in mouth	9"h	200-250			
1209.	Scottie dog Reg No 778504 Nov 1932	11"h	90-180			
1209.	Scottie dog as 1209 with golf ball in mouth	11"h	250-300			
1210.	Jar vase	7.5"h	10-20			
1211.	Bowl	1.75"h	5-8			

Mould No	Description	Size	Price Guide in £'s	Colour	Date Purchased	Price Paid
1212.	Candle holder ribbed	4"h	10-20			
1213.	Covered butter dish		10-18			
1214.	Flower pot ribbed	7"dia	20-25			
1215.	Flower pot ribbed	8.75"dia	20-25			
1216.	Biscuit barrel ribbed	7"h	20-30			
1217.	N/I					
1218.	Dutch clog		10-15			
1219.	N/I					
1220.	N/I					
1221.	Gnome with wheelbarrow	8"h	70-120			
1222.	Goblin similar to 842 (Billikins)	5.75"h	55-80			
1223.	N/I					
1224.	N/I					
1225.	N/I					
1226.	Wall plaque clown	9"h 6"w	150-250			
1227.	Dog Labrador standing	5"h	60-90			
1228.	N/I					
1229.	N/I					
1230.	Toby jug 'Sarah Gamp'		60-140			
1231.	Toby jug 'Sam Weller'	6.5"h	60-140			
1232.	N/I					
1233.	N/I					
1234.	N/I					

Mould No	Description	Size	Price Guide in £'s	Colour	Date Purchased	Price Paid
1235.	Posy diamond shape	10"l 2"h	8-10			
1236.	N/I					
1237.	Figures bride and groom		85-140			
1238.	Elephant on one leg, in football clothes	8"h	300-350			
1239.	N/I					
1240.	Bunny with vase embossed trees on vase	6.5"h	90-140			
1241.	N/I					
1242.	N/I					
1243.	Dog tall with collar	9"h	65-90			
1244.	Dog tall with collar	10.5"h	70-100			
1245.	Dog Scottie	5.75"h	70-120			
1246.	Dog 'Sammy' Reg No 813261 1936	4.5"h	30-40			
1247.	Dog 'Sammy' Reg No 813261 1936	5.5"h	50-65			
1248.	Posy ring	8"dia	8-12			
1249.	Posy bowl	6"dia	8-10			
1250.	Posy holder round	6"dia	5-7			
1251.	Posy diamond shape	7"l	8-10			
1252.	Flower jug	6"h	15-25			
1253.	Flower jug ribbed	6.25"h	10-15			
1254.	Flower jug ribbed	6"h	10-15			
1255.	Rabbit mat holder and mats	5.5"h	80-120			
1256.	N/I					
1257.	Round vase	7.75"h	10-15			

Mould No	Description	Size	Price Guide in £'s	Colour	Date Purchased	Price Paid
1258.	Sailor and rum keg	9"h	100-150			
1259.	Dog Scottie	2.75"h	20-35			
1260.	N/I					
1261.	Dog Scottie standing	7.75"h	80-130			
1262.	Dog Scottie standing	8"h	120-180			
1263.	N/I					
1264.	Jug size 3	4.25"h	15-20			
1265.	Hare 'Harry the Hare'	3"h	25-45			
1266.	Ash Tray		10-15			
1267.	Flower pot round ribbed	8"dia	15-20			
1268.	Flower pot round ribbed	9"dia	18-25			
1269.	Flower pot round ribbed	10"dia	20-30			
1270.	Hare match holder	3"h	30-45			
1271.	Vase for spills	5"h	15-25			
1272.	Deco style vase shell design	7.25"h	30-65			
1273.	Flower jug 'Rope' range	6"h	20-35			
1274.	Flower jug hollyhock	8.5"h	30-65			
1275.	Deco vase shell design	6"h	20-50			
1276.	Deco flower jug shell design	6"h	30-40			
1277.	Deco flower jug shell design as 1276	7"h	30-40			
1278.	Fruit bowl shell design	11"dia	20-40			
1279.	Flower trough shell design	12.5"l	15-25			
1280.	Deco vase shell design	8.5"h	30-60			

Mould No	Description	Size	Price Guide in £'s	Colour	Date Purchased	Price Paid
1281.	Lamb		30-50			
1281.	Deco flower jug shell design as 1276	9.75"h	40-70			
1282.	Flower pot shell design	8.5"dia	25-45			
1283.	Flower pot shell design	9.5"dia	25-45			
1284.	Lamb two designs	4"h	35-55			
1285.	Lamb as 1284	5"h	40-60			
1286.	Cat with collar	4"h	200-250			
1287.	Cat Similar to 1286		70-100			
1288.	Mini character jug candle holder	3.5"h	25-40			
1289.	Mini character jug	2.75"h	25-40			
1290.	Eagle	4"h	70-120			
1291.	Dog caricature	3.5"h	100-150			
1292.	Chick ash tray/bowl	4.25"h	70-120			
1293.	Duck ash tray	3.5"h	70-100			
1294.	Rabbit ash tray/bowl	5.5"l	70-100			
1295.	Dog Scottie/Griffon, sitting	5"h	40-65			
1296.	Kittens in a basket	4"h	45-65			
1297.	N/I					
1298.	Harry the hare Reg No 815840 1936	5.75"h	35-60			
1299.	Harry the hare Reg No 815840 1936	7.75"h	100-180			
1300.	Harry the hare Reg No 815840 1936	9.5"h	250-350			
1301.	Jug		10-25			
1302.	Lop-eared rabbit Reg No 815839 1936	5.5"h	40-60			

Mould No	Description	Size	Price Guide in £'s	Colour	Date Purchased	Price Paid
1303.	Lop-eared rabbit Reg No 815839 1936	7"h	90-120			
1304.	Lop-eared rabbit Reg No 815839 1936	8.5"h	150-220			
1305.	Flower jug bird and nest	8"h	250-300			
1306.	Vase 'Rope' range	5.5"h	20-35			
1307.	Deco vase 'Rope' range	8.5"h	20-35			
1308.	Vase 'Rope' range	5.5"h	20-35			
1309.	Vase 'Rope' range	7.75"h	20-35			
1310.	Jug 'Rope' range	6"h	20-40			
1311.	Book-end bunnies etc	4.5"h	70-90			
1311.	Book-end others	5"h	70-90			
1312.	Round posy with 3 rabbits round edge	8.25"dia	40-60			
1312.	Round posy with Scottie round edge	8.25"dia	40-65			
1312.	Round posy with Seagull round edge	8.25"dia	40-65			
1313.	Cat as 1046 scared	16"h	400-800			
1314.	Posy trough	1.5"h 4.5"l	5-8			
1315.	Posy	6"l	4-6			
1316.	Posy	8"l	5-7			
1317.	Posy	12"l	5-10			
1318.	Flower jug bunnies on handle	8.75"h	50-70			
1319.	Figure sailor		70-150			
1320.	Shoe ashtray	2"h	10-15			
1321.	Loving cup commemorative George VI 1937	6.25"h	50-60			
1322.	Toast rack	6.5"l	15-25			

Mould No	Description	Size	Price Guide in £'s	Colour	Date Purchased	Price Paid
1323.	Pot		10-15			
1324.	Posy trough angled	11"l	10-15			
1325.	Posy trough diamond shape	10"l	10-15			
1326.	Posy holder with figure	3.5"h	60-95			
1327.	Deco style vase with figure on one end	8.75"l	40-50			
1327.	Long vase as above with various animals	8.75"l	20-30			
1328.	Bird Kingfisher	4"h	75-120			
1329.	Bird Falcon		75-120			
1330.	Bird Kingfisher	4"h	75-120			
1331.	Bird Duck	6.25"h	75-120			
1332.	Caricature Dachshund	5.25"h 5"l	75-150			
1333.	Cat crouching	4"h	85-160			
1334.	Foal standing	4"h	20-45			
1335.	Hip flask	4"h	15-25			
1336.	Posy with figure holder	7.25"h	75-150			
1337.	Posy holder with flower seller	6.25"h	75-150			
1338.	Yacht solid as 1339	6"h	30-50			
1339.	Yacht solid with no posy holder	8.75"h	40-60			
1340.	Yacht posy holder similar to 1393 & 1394	12.5"h	125-175			
1341.	Vase deco style	5.25"h	25-35			
1342.	Jug triple handle	6.75"h	25-45			
1343.	Vase deco diagonal lines	9"h	25-45			
1344.	Jug	9"h	25-45			

Mould No	Description	Size	Price Guide in £'s	Colour	Date Purchased	Price Paid
1345.	Vase deco style	9"h	15-25			
1346.	Vase Deco style	10.5"h	15-30			
1347.	Vase		15-25			
1348.	Jug Deco style	12.5"h	30-45			
1349.	Seagull Reg No 823083	3"h	50-85			
1350.	Seagull Reg No 823083	4"h	60-100			
1351.	Seagull Reg No 823083	5"h	85-200			
1352.	Posy holder Reg No 823084	6"h	30-40			
1353.	Twin posy holder Reg No 823082	6"h	50-60			
1354.	N/I					
1355.	Vase 'Autumn' range	7"h	30-50			
1356.	Jug 'Autumn' range	6"h	25-45			
1357.	Seagull similar to 1351,1350,1349	2.25"h	30-50			
1358.	Plant pot 'Autumn' range	8.25"h	25-45			
1359.	Jug 'Autumn' range similar to 1356	12"h	30-50			
1360.	Flying duck similar to 1402,1401,1403	12"l	90-120			
1361.	Cruet 3 piece on tray		20-30			
1362.	Sugar shaker deco style	5"h	15-25			
1363.	Jug deco style	7.25"h	25-35			
1364.	Mug to go with 1363	3.25"h	8-10			
1365.	Jam pot deco style	4.25"h	10-15			
1366.	Ashtray with various animals	5.75"l	20-45			
1366.	Bird More information needed					

Mould No	Description	Size	Price Guide in £'s	Colour	Date Purchased	Price Paid
1367.	Jug	6"h	10-15			
1368.	Covered bowl to match 1362 deco style	4.25"dia	15-25			
1369.	Dog Alsatian sitting puppy	5"h	35-70			
1370.	Budgerigar jug	7.5"h	80-150			
1371.	Hare crouching	3.5"h	80-120			
1372.	Polar bear	2.75"h	30-45			
1373.	Goat standing	4"l	50-80			
1374.	Donkey	4"l	60-90			
1375.	Bird duck	3.5"h	80-160			
1376.	Bird pigeon	3"h	80-160			
1377.	Bird pigeon	4"h	80-160			
1378.	Dog Terrier sitting	5"h	20-35			
1379.	Dog Terrier sitting	8"h	45-75			
1380.	Dog Terrier sitting	11"h	130-170			
1381.	Wall pocket	7.25"h	30-50			
1382.	Dog Spaniel sitting	8"h	45-95			
1383.	N/I					
1384.	Wall pocket deco sun ray like 1109	7.25"h	70-110			
1385.	Wall pocket ribbed deco like 1150		40-60			
1386.	Rabbit	3.25"h	25-55			
1387.	N/I					
1388.	Hare crouching	5.5"h	150-200			
1389.	Hare crouching	7.5"h	200-350			

Mould No	Description	Size	Price Guide in £'s	Colour	Date Purchased	Price Paid
1390.	Koala bear on a log	4.5"h	45-70			
1391.	Koala bear on a log	6"h	50-80			
1392.	Toast rack Deco	2.5"h 6.5"l	35-55			
1393.	Yacht posy holder like 1340 Reg No 826482	5.75"h	35-45			
1394.	Yacht posy holder like 1340 Reg No 826482	8.5"h	45-70			
1395.	Wall pocket with flowers or without flowers	6.25"h	50-85 20-30			
1396.	N/I					
1397.	Horse shoe shape posy		8-10			
1398.	Wall plaque Rabbit		120-180			
1399.	Frog crouching	2.5"h	65-95			
1400.	Tinies, combi-number for a Selection of miniatures	1.5"h	20-50			
1401.	Wall plaque duck like 1360,1402,1403	6.5"l	35-85			
1402.	Wall plaque duck as above	9.5"l	45-100			
1403.	Wall plaque duck as above	5"l	30-65			
1403.	Seal vase/posy	3.5"h 4.5"l	80-120			
1404.	Jug	6.5"h	12-18			
1405.	Jug deco similar to 1404/6	8.5"h	20-35			
1406.	Jug Deco	11"h	20-30			
1407.	Vase serpent design	8.5"h	15-20			
1408.	Vase serpent design	10.5"h	30-40			
1409.	Jug	5.25"h	20-30			
1410.	Jug	8"h	20-35			
1411.	Jug similar to 1409/10	10.5"h	30-45			

Mould No	Description	Size	Price Guide in £'s	Colour	Date Purchased	Price Paid
1412.	Dog Airedale Terrier	9"h	200-250			
1413.	Vase triple tree trunk	4.5"h	35-45			
1414.	Dog sitting Scottie	5"h	45-60			
1415.	Dog standing Cairn	5"h	40-60			
1416.	Vase tree trunk with Koala Bear	5"h	50-90			
1417.	Jug	6"h	15-25			
1418.	Jug	8.25"h	15-25			
1419.	Jug deco	11.25"h	35-50			
1420.	Lucky Pixie with toadstool & squirrel	3"h	25-35			
1421.	Lucky Pixie sitting on mound	3"h	30-40			
1422.	Horse sitting similar to 1447	4.75"h	60-100			
1423.	Bear standing	3"h	40-55			
1424.	Fox crouching	2.25"h	40-75			
1425.	Hippo standing	3"h	60-110			
1426.	Bear or Panda standing	3.25"h	40-60			
1427.	Lamb looking at tail	4.75"h	75-120			
1428.	Donkey standing	4.25"h	25-35			
1429.	Vase tall diamond shape	9"h	20-35			
1430.	N/I					
1431.	Calf standing back	3.5"h	35-60			
1432.	Cat three models	2"h	20-35			
1433.	Dog one paw in sling	3.5"h	25-45			
1434.	Cat lying down		25-35			

Mould No	Description	Size	Price Guide in £'s	Colour	Date Purchased	Price Paid.
1435.	Jug for cider 'Barrel' range	8"h	25-30			
1436.	Mug 'Barrel' range go with 1435	3.5"h	8-12			
1437.	Jam pot 'Barrel' range		12-17			
1438.	Butter dish round 'Barrel' range		10-15			
1439.	Cruet 4 piece 'Barrel' range	4.5"dia 1.75"h	35-65			
1440.	Butter dish/sweet tray 'Barrel' range	4"l	6-10			
1441.	Cigarette Barrel	3"h	8-10			
1442.	Match holder 'Barrel' range	1.75"h	10-12			
1443.	Sauce bottle holder 'Barrel' range	3.75"h	8-12			
1444.	N/I					
1445.	Sauce boat 'Barrel' range	5.25"l	10-12			
1446.	Biscuit jar 'Barrel' range	7"h	15-25			
1447.	Foal lying down	3.5"h	25-50			
1448.	Bowl	5.5"h	10-25			
1449.	Flower stand to go with 1448 not sold sep					
1450.	Dog small Scottie		25-35			
1451.	Stag standing	5.25"h	50-80			
1452.	Jug Mr. Pickwick	6"h	30-65			
1453.	Jug Mr. Micawber	6"h	30-65			
1454.	Ashtray round with animal (various)	5.25"l	15-30			
1455.	Ashtray as pond with animal(s)	4.75"dia	15-35			
1456.	Bridge set trays clubs,heart,spade & diamond		30-50			
1456.	Mug 'Barrel' range	3.5"h	8-10			

Mould No	Description	Size	Price Guide in £'s	Colour	Date Purchased	Price Paid
1457.	Holder two tree stumps with two bunnies	3"h	50-75			
1458.	Leopard attending to foot	9.5"h	200-400			
1459.	Serviette ring with hare	3"h	25-35			
1460.	N/I					
1461.	Dog Spaniel	6"h	40-60			
1462.	Dog Spaniel	11"h	220-290			
1463.	Jug Neville Chamberlain	6.25"h	30-90			
1464.	Tortoise one piece	3.25"l 2.5"h	75-100			
1465.	Alligator		75-100			
1466.	Chameleon on branch	7"l	75-100			
1467.	Lizard	7.25"l	80-100			
1468.	N/I					
1469.	N/I					
1470.	Cruet pepper and salt		20-25			
1471.	N/I					
1472.	Car ashtray	1.5"h 5"l	100-150			
1473.	Basket large shaped10"l	6"h	30-60			
1474.	Dog similar 1475,1476	6.75"h	50-80			
1474.	Holder with cat		25-35			
1475.	Dog similar to 1474, 1476 sitting with paw raised	7.75"h	80-150			
1476.	Dog similar to 1475,1474 sitting with paw raised	11"h	250-350			
1477.	N/I					
1478.	Twin vase alone with animals	3.25"h 20-40	10-20			

Mould No	Description	Size	Price Guide in £'s	Colour	Date Purchased	Price Paid
1479.	Posy curved, various animals	8.5"l	25-35			
1479.	Posy curved, with lady	8.5"l	20-35			
1480.	Posy round with gnome in centre	5.75"dia	15-30			
1481.	Posy round with gnome in centre	8.75"dia	25-35			
1482.	Candlestick		15-25			
1482.	Ashtray with lines		8-10			
1483.	N/l					
1484.	Top Hat with kitten Reg No 833892	4"h	25-35			
1485.	Candlestick with animal/flower	4"h	30-50			
1486.	Pig sitting		35-45			
1487.	Posy log with Koala Bear	6.5"l 4.5"h	40-60			
1488.	Posy	3.5"l	10-15			
1489.	Vase	4.5"h	15-20			
1490.	Vase	4.75"h	10-15			
1491.	Vase	4.75"h	10-15			
1492.	Duck Reg No 833893. similar to 1498,1499	5"h	95-120			
1493.	Kangaroo		100-180			
1494.	Squirrel eating from bowl	4"h	30-40			
1495.	Vase		15-25			
1496.	Basket	7"h	15-25			
1497.	Rabbit one ear forward crouching	3"l	90-150			
1498.	Duck Reg No 833893 similar to 1492,1499	3.25"h	50-70			
1499.	Duck Reg No 833893 similar to 1492,1498	4.25"h	65-95			

Mould No	Description	Size	Price Guide in £'s	Colour	Date Purchased	Price Paid
1500.	Panda standing	8"l 4.5"h	50-65			
1501.	N/I					
1502.	Dog with paw in sling	7.25"h	150-200			
1503.	N/I					
1504.	Dog front paw in wicker basket	3.5"h	40-60			
1505.	Lambs set of six (small)	1.5"h	250-300			
1506.	Panda sitting	5.5"h	50-70			
1507.	N/I					
1508.	Small foal standing	5"h	45-65			
1509.	Lop eared rabbit	3.75"h	30-45			
1510.	Mushroom vase with lop eared rabbit	5.5"h	35-45			
1511.	Rabbit sitting up ear lying back as 1525/6	13"h	300-400			
1512.	Dog half lying down	3"h	55-70			
1513.	Plant pot holder with rabbits & gnomes	7"dia	25-40			
1514.	Plant pot holder with rabbits & gnomes	8.5"dia	35-45			
1514.	Plant pot holder as above with frogs		40-55			
1515.	N/I					
1516.	N/I					
1517.	Ashtray squirrel on one side	4.75"h	35-40			
1518.	Squirrel holding nut	3.5"h	35-55			
1519.	Stag astride rock	4.75h	90-140			
1520.	Bear sitting	2.25"h	30-45			
1521.	Bear on back with feet in air	1.5"h	30-45			

Mould No	Description	Size	Price Guide in £'s	Colour	Date Purchased	Price Paid
1522.	Bear standing on all fours	1.75"h	30-45			
1523.	Rabbit hunched up like 1530	4.5"h	180-300			
1524.	Dog one paw tied in sling	6"h	100-130			
1525.	Rabbit sitting up ear lying back as 1511/26	8.5"h	150-200			
1526.	Rabbit sitting up ear lying back as 1511/25	10.5"h	200-300			
1527.	Elephant sitting back	3.5"h	80-100			
1528.	Dog Scratching with back leg	3.5"h	80-100			
1529.	Rabbit hunched up like 1523/30	3.5"h	100-130			
1530.	Rabbit hunched up like 1523/9	5.5"h	350-400			
1531.	Ashtray banjo shape	5.75"l	15-25			
1532.	Ashtray with two bunnies nose to nose	3.25"h	40-50			
1533.	Dog	13.75"h	400-600			
1534.	Bunnies nose to nose	2.5"h	30-45			
1535.	Dog collie		30-50			
1536.	N/I					
1537.	N/I					
1538.	Vase	3.5"h	10-15			
1539.	N/I					
1540.	Vase posy with stag attached	5.5"h	100-130			
1541.	Bowl round	3"dia	10-15			
1542.	Bowl similar to above	4"dia	10-15			
1543.	Wall plaque seagull as 1544/5	4.5"l	40-50			
1544.	Wall plaque seagull as 1543/5	7.25"l	65-80			

Mould No	Description	Size	Price Guide in £'s	Colour	Date Purchased	Price Paid
1545.	Wall plaque seagull as 1543/4	8.5"l	65-120			
1546.	Book support (pair) with 'Lop Eared Rabbit'	4.5"h	70-100			
1546.	Book support (pair) with dog		70-100			
1547.	Ashtray musical instrument	5.75"l	15-25			
1548.	Dog Collie standing on all fours	5.25"h	30-50			
1549.	Vase		10-20			
1550.	Vase		10-20			
1551.	Small jug	3"h	9-12			
1552.	Round mug	3"h	9-12			
1553.	Small jug	3"h	9-12			
1554-1556	N/I					
1557.	Shaving mug		20-30			
1558.	N/I					
1559.	Jug	9"h	20-30			
1560.	N/I					
1561.	Dish flower shape	4.25"dia	5-8			
1562.	Vase	8"h	8-10			
1563.	Vase round	10"h	10-20			
1564.	Vase	11.75"h	15-25			
1565.	Bowl oval	5.5"h	20-30			
1566.	Vase posy embossed boat on wave	4.75"h	30-40			
1567.	N/I					
1568.	Vase similar to 1570	5"h	10-20			

Mould No	Description	Size	Price Guide in £'s	Colour	Date Purchased	Price Paid
1569.	Vase		10-20			
1570.	Vase one handle	7"h	10-20			
1571.	Vase	10"h	10-25			
1572.	Salt, pepper and mustard on tray 'Dahlia' range		20-35			
1573.	Ashtray in the shape of armchair	3.75"h	25-45			
1574.	N/I					
1575.	Vase	6"h	10-20			
1576.	N/I					
1577.	N/I					
1578.	Vase round with turn marks	8"h	15-25			
1579.	Mug 'Dahlia' range	3.5"h	8-10			
1580.	Jugs 3 sizes 'Dahlia' range	4.25 - 6.25"h	10-25			
1581.	Jam/honey pot 'Dahlia' range	4.5"h	10-15			
1582.	Butter dish 'Dahlia' range	4.5"dia	10-15			
1583.	Open sugar 'Dahlia' range	3.25"dia	8-10			
1584.	Small jug 'Dahlia' range	4.5"h	10-15			
1585.	Tea pot 'Dahlia' range	6"h	20-30			
1586.	Cheese cover/ dish rectangular 'Dahlia' range	7.25"l	15-25			
1587.	Biscuit barrel 'Dahlia' range	6.5"h	15-25			
1588.	Pot 'Dahlia' range	5"h	10-15			
1589.	Small stackable bowl set with lid	4"dia	10-15			
1590.	Match holder pair rabbits	2.5"h	30-40			
1591.	Dish rectangular usually lidded	7"l	10-20			

Mould No	Description	Size	Price Guide in £'s	Colour	Date Purchased	Price Paid
1592.	N/I					
1593.	N/I					
1594.	Ashtray mounted with dog or rabbit		25-35			
1595.	Milk jug 'Dahlia' range	8"h	12-20			
1596.	N/I					
1597.	Vase 'Dahlia' range	4"h	10-15			
1598.	N/I					
1599.	Basket 'Dahlia' range	5.25"h 9.5"l	30-45			
1600.	Mug (no handle) 'Dahlia' range	4.5"h	10-15			
1601.	N/I					
1602.	N/I					
1603.	Lamp base Embossed flowers	7"h	30-40			
1604.	N/I					
1605.	Jug 'Dahlia' range	6.5"h	15-25			
1606.	Jug 'Dahlia' range	7.25"	15-25			
1607.	Vase 'Dahlia' range	9.5"h	15-25			
1608.	Wall plaque garland with kissing bunnies		150-200			
1609.	N/I					
1610.	Basket small		10-15			
1611.	Wall pocket		25-35			
1612.	Jug	7"h	10-20			
1613.	Wall vase 'Dahlia' range	4"h	25-35			
1614.	Mug D'ye ken John Peel	4"h	15-25			

Mould No	Description	Size	Price Guide in £'s	Colour	Date Purchased	Price Paid
1615.	Vase		10-20			
1616.	N/I					
1617.	N/I					
1618.	Jug		10-20			
1619.	N/I					
1620.	Vase asymmetrical	11"h	15-20			
1621.	N/I					
1622.	Ashtray as fireplace with animal		35-50			
1622.	Ashtray as fireplace		25-30			
1623.	Jug	6"h	15-20			
1624.	Jug	6"h	10-20			
1625.	Jug	6"h	10-20			
1626.	Vase	8.75h	10-20			
1627.	Vase		10-20			
1628.	Vase		10-20			
1629.	N/I					
1630.	Wishing well		30-50			
1631-1634	N/I					
1635.	Plant pot	6"h 11"l	15-25			
1636.	N/I					
1637.	Vase		10-20			
1638.	N/I					
1639.	N/I					

Mould No	Description	Size	Price Guide in £'s	Colour	Date Purchased	Price Paid
1640.	Jug	7"h	10-20			
1641.	Jug	6"h	10-20			
1642.	N/I					
1643.	Flower jug 'Dahlia' range	10.75"h	15-30			
1644.	Tall vase 'Dahlia' range	8.5"h	15-25			
1645.	Vase tall		10-20			
1646.	Dog small puppy playing	3"h	30-60			
1647.	Dog puppy eyes closed	3.5"h	80-120			
1648-1650	N/I					
1651.	Vase embossed	7.25"h	10-20			
1652.	Pot/vase two handles 'Dahlia' range	5.75"h	15-20			
1653.	Long bowl embossed	5.5"h	10-20			
1654.	Dish with two handles	5"dia	10-15			
1655.	Flower jug embossed flowers	8"h	15-25			
1656.	Flower jug	6"h	15-25			
1657.	Basket		15-20			
1658.	N/I					
1659.	Lamb head turned	3.75" h	35-55			
1660.	Lamb	6"h	90-120			
1660.	Toastrack		12-20			
1661.	Lamb like 1659 Reg No 838603 year 1941	8"h	200-250			
1662.	N/I					
1663.	Airman	6"h	130-180			

Mould No	Description	Size	Price Guide in £'s	Colour	Date Purchased	Price Paid
1664.	Soldier	5.5"h	130-180			
1665.	N/I					
1666.	N/I					
1667.	Ashtray seen with various figures	5"dia	25-40			
1668-1671	N/I					
1672.	Candle holder		10-20			
1673-1675	N/I					
1676.	Lamp base art deco		20-30			
1677.	N/I					
1678.	Duck skiing	2"h	75-100			
1679.	Duck skiing	2.75"h	100-140			
1680.	Duck skiing	5.25"h	150-200			
1681.	Duck (without skis)		75-100			
1682.	Duck (without skis)		100-140			
1683.	Duck (without skis)		150-200			
1684.	Jug bulbous base	9"h	15-25			
1685.	Jug embossed	7"h	10-20			
1686.	Vase		10-20			
1687-1690	N/I					
1691.	Lemonade jug To go with mug		15-25			
1691.	Lemonade mug To go with jug		10-15			
1692.	N/I					
1693.	Teapot leaf design	5.5"h	20-40			

Mould No	Description	Size	Price Guide in £'s	Colour	Date Purchased	Price Paid
1694.	N/I					
1695.	Bowl/honey two handled sugar	3"h	8-15			
1696.	Bowl/butter dish two handles	4"h	10-15			
1697.	Jug		10-20			
1698.	Jug 'Green Leaf' design	3"h	8-15			
1699.	Sugar bowl	4"dia	8-10			
1700.	Sugar bowl	3.5"dia	8-10			
1701.	Flower jug		20-30			
1702.	N/I					
1703.	Teapot		25-35			
1704.	Sugar bowl fluted		8-10			
1705.	Jug		10-20			
1706.	Butter dish lid as spokes of wheel		10-15			
1707-1709	N/I					
1710.	Jug	10"h	20-30			
1711.	Mug embossed	3.5"h	8-10			
1712.	N/I					
1713.	Plate	1.25"l	8-10			
1714.	Bowl		8-10			
1715.	Salt, pepper, mustard & tray dogs heads on boxes		90-110			
1716.	Jug		10-20			
1717.	Mug		8-12			
1718.	N/I					

Mould No	Description	Size	Price Guide in £'s	Colour	Date Purchased	Price Paid
1719.	Vase embossed leaves	5.5"h	10-15			
1720.	Cruet with handle		15-20			
1721.	N/I					
1722.	N/I					
1723.	Lamp		20-40			
1724.	Lamp with tree and rabbits	8"h	80-140			
1725.	Salt and Pepper ? with tray		20-25			
1726.	N/I					
1727.	Lamp base embossed flowers	5.75"h	30-40			
1727.	Teapot		35-40			
1728.	Jug 'Barrel' range	3.25"h	10-15			
1729.	Jug		10-20			
1730.	N/I					
1731.	Vase		10-20			
1732.	Vase	9"h	15-20			
1733.	Tray		8-10			
1734-1736	N/I					
1737.	Jug		10-20			
1738.	Bowl on three feet	8"dia	10-18			
1739-1743	N/I					
1744.	Jug	5.5"h	10-20			
1745.	Jug raised bumps	6"h	10-20			
1746.	Jug embossed flower	6"h	10-20			

Mould No	Description	Size	Price Guide in £'s	Colour	Date Purchased	Price Paid
1747.	Cheese dish embossed 'Neptune' ware		20-35			
1748.	Tray embossed 'Neptune' ware	12"l	15-25			
1749.	Teapot		20-35			
1750.	N/I					
1751.	Flower jug		15-20			
1752.	Basket		15-20			
1753.	N/I					
1754.	Bowl small		5-10			
1755.	Basket		10-15			
1756.	Jug		10-20			
1757.	Vase with wave pattern lines	6"h	10-15			
1758.	Vase diagonal ridges	6"h	10-15			
1759.	N/I					
1760.	Covered bowl		12-16			
1761.	N/I					
1762.	N/I					
1763.	Vase		10-20			
1764.	N/I					
1765.	Small bowl for sugar		5-10			
1766.	N/I					
1767.	Dish rectangular with dragon	13"l	60-85			
1768.	Sweet dish		5-10			
1769.	Butter dish		15-20			

Mould No	Description	Size	Price Guide in £'s	Colour	Date Purchased	Price Paid
1770.	Bowl for sugar		5-10			
1771.	Mug		8-10			
1772.	N/I					
1773.	Basket		10-20			
1774.	Bowl 'Cavalier' range	5"h	20-35			
1775.	Beer mug 'Cavalier' range	5"h	15-25			
1776.	Cheese dish 'Primrose' range		15-25			
1777.	Basket woven effect	3.5"h	15-20			
1778.	Jug		10-20			
1779.	Jug dragon wrapped round	9"h	60-95			
1780.	Basket embossed flowers	5.5"h	10-15			
1781.	Vase embossed flowers	6.5"h	10-20			
1782.	Jug embossed flowers	6.5"h	10-20			
1783.	Bowl embossed flowers	4"h	5-10			
1784.	Jug deco	6.25"h	15-20			
1785.	N/I					
1786.	Vase	4.5"h	8-12			
1787.	Vase deco, two handles	4.25"h	10-15			
1788.	N/I					
1789.	N/I					
1790.	Jug		10-20			
1791.	Dish embossed	4.25"l	10-20			
1792.	N/I					

Mould No	Description	Size	Price Guide in £'s	Colour	Date Purchased	Price Paid
1793.	N/I					
1794.	Jug	4.5"h	15-20			
1795.	Jug	6"h	10-20			
1796.	Basket	4.25"h	15-20			
1797.	Dish embossed 'Neptune' ware		10-15			
1798.	Double tray embossed 'Neptune' ware		15-25			
1799.	N/I					
1800.	N/I					
1801.	Jug 'Cavalier' range	8"h	15-25			
1802.	N/I					
1803.	Vase		10-20			
1804.	N/I					
1805.	N/I					
1806.	N/I					
1807.	Vase	9.75"h	15-25			
1808.	Vase 'Dovedale' range	8"h	15-30			
1809.	N/I					
1810.	N/I					
1811.	N/I					
1812.	Teapot 'Neptune' ware	5.5"h	25-35			
1813.	Bowl small 'Neptune' ware	2.25"h	5-12			
1814.	Jug small to go with 1813 'Neptune' ware	2.5"h	5-12			
1815.	Jug three sizes 'Neptune' ware		10-25			

Mould No	Description	Size	Price Guide in £'s	Colour	Date Purchased	Price Paid
1816.	N/I					
1817.	Vase		10-20			
1818.	Butter dish round with dog's head, as 1715		35-55			
1819.	Basket	4"h	8-12			
1820.	Trinket box floral lid	3.25"h	25-35			
1821.	Powder bowl floral	3.75"h	25-35			
1822.	Dish small floral	5"l	15-20			
1823.	Bowl	4"dia	10-15			
1824.	Jug	8.75"h	15-25			
1825.	Ashtray with or without flowers		15-20			
1826.	Rose bowl diamond shape with trellis	5"h	15-25			
1827.	Bowl	3.5"h	10-15			
1828.	N/I					
1829.	Basket	9"l	15-25			
1830.	Bowl	8.5"l	10-20			
1831.	Vase leaf handles	6.5"h	15-25			
1832.	Vase two handles	8.25	15-25			
1833.	Vase two handles asymmetrical	8.5"h	15-25			
1834.	Vase	8.5"h	15-25			
1835.	Vase two handles asymmetrical	8.5"h	15-25			
1836.	Vase	8.5"h	15-25			
1837.	Vase	8.5"h	15-25			
1838-1847	N/I					

Mould No	Description	Size	Price Guide in £'s	Colour	Date Purchased	Price Paid
1848.	Bowl	3"dia	10-20			
1848.	Bowl With 5/7 flowers	3"dia	10-20 20-30			
1849.	Preserve pot dog's head lid as 1715/8	4.25"h	40-60			
1850.	Cheese dish dog's head lid, rectangular	6.5"l	40-60			
1851.	Bowl/basket 'Wild Duck' range	8.5"l	20-35			
1852.	Bowl 'Wild Duck' range	8"l	20-35			
1853.	Vase 'Wild Duck' range	6.5"h	15-20			
1854.	Jug 'Wild Duck' range	8.5"h	20-30			
1856.	Vase 'Wild Duck' range	5"h	15-20			
1857.	Vase 'Wild Duck' range	8.5"h	20-30			
1857.	Lamp base as above 'Wild Duck' range	8.5"h	40-50			
1858.	Vase 'Wild Duck' range	8.5"h	20-30			
1859.	Vase.....diamond shape 'Wild Duck' range	5"h	15-20			
1860.	Bowl.....diamond shape 'Wild Duck' range	9.5"l	20-30			
1861.	Tray.....diamond shape 'Blackberry' range	12.5"l	15-25			
1862.	Dish 'Blackberry' range	10.75"l	20-25			
1863.	N/I					
1864.	Dish square 'Blackberry' range	8.5"dia	20-25			
1865.	Plate 'Blackberry' range	5.5"	10-12			
1866.	Jug 'Blackberry' range		15-25			
1867.	Preserve pot 'Blackberry' range	4.5"h	18-25			
1868.	Lidded Butter 'Blackberry' range	3"h	15-25			
1869.	Cream jug 'Blackberry' range	2.75"h	15-20			

Mould No	Description	Size	Price Guide in £'s	Colour	Date Purchased	Price Paid
1870.	Preserve pot 'Blackberry' range	3.5"h	10-20			
1871. 'Blackberry' range	Sugar bowl	2"h	10-20			
1872.	Cheese dish 'Blackberry' range	6.5"l	20-30			
1873.	Toastrack 'Blackberry' range	5.25"l	20-25			
1874.	Double dish 'Blackberry' range	10.5"l	20-25			
1875.	Jug set leaf 3 sizes		25-45			
1876.	Jug 'Blackberry' range 3 sizes		15-20			
1877.	Shaving mug	3.25'h	35-45			
1878.	Mug 'Blackberry' range		15-20			
1879.	Bowl with lid 'Blackberry' range		15-25			
1880.	N/I					
1881.	N/I					
1882.	Candle holder	1"h	15-25			
1883.	Vase		10-12			
1884.	Teapot		30-40			
1885.	N/I					
1886.	Coffee pot 'Blackberry' range		35-40			
1887.	Butter and toast tray embossed leaf		15-20			
1888.	Honey/jam pot embossed leaf		8-12			
1889.	Teapot large leaf design		30-45			
1890.	Jug large leaf design	2.5"h	12-20			
1891.	Sugar bowl		8-10			
1892.	Posy ring		8-10			

Mould No	Description	Size	Price Guide in £'s	Colour	Date Purchased	Price Paid
1893.	Posy ring		8-10			
1894.	Dish With animals or flowers	6"l	10-20			
1895.	N/I					
1896.	Hawthorn tree and bird		40-70			
1897.	Ashtray With novelty or flowers	5"dia	10-25			
1898.	Dish raised floral	5.5"dia	10-15			
1899.	Posy		10-15			
1900.	N/I					
1901.	Vase		10-20			
1902.	N/I					
1903.	Floral Box diamond shape	2.25"h	20-30			
1904.	Jug		10-20			
1905.	Lamp base		10-20			
1906.	N/I					
1907.	Tray		10-15			
1908.	Coffee cup 'Blackberry' range	2.5"h	15-20			
1909.	Floral posy	2.5"h	10-15			
1910.	Dish open flower shape	4.5"dia	15-25			
1911-1914	N/I					
1915.	Biscuit barrel		20-35			
1916.	Biscuit barrel		20-35			
1917.	N/I					
1918.	Biscuit barrel	8"h	20-35			

Mould No	Description	Size	Price Guide in £'s	Colour	Date Purchased	Price Paid
1919.	Floral dish	6.75"dia	25-40			
1920.	Floral dish	5"dia	20-30			
1921.	Floral dish	7.5"dia	25-45			
1922.	Vase posy	2"h	5-10			
1923.	Plant pot	2.5"h	10-15			
1924.	Bowl ribbed	3"dia	8-10			
1925.	N/I					
1926.	Jug		10-20			
1927.	N/I					
1928.	N/I					
1929.	Teapot		20-40			
1930.	Floral posy bowl		15-25			
1931.	Box		10-15			
1932.	N/I					
1933.	Dish open flower shape	6"dia	20-30			
1934.	Dish open flower shape	7"dia	25-35			
1935.	Tray in shape of log		15-20			
1936.	Mug		8-10			
1937.	Honey/jam pot 'Hobnail' range	4.5"h	10-15			
1938.	Jug 'Hobnail' range		10-20			
1939.	Bowl small, 'Hobnail' range		8-12			
1940.	N/I					
1941.	Butter dish		8-10			

Mould No	Description	Size	Price Guide in £'s	Colour	Date Purchased	Price Paid
1942.	Teapot		25-35			
1943.	Set of 3 Jugs 'Hobnail' range		25-45			
1944.	N/l					
1945.	Cider Jug		20-35			
1946.	Cheese dish 'Hobnail' range		15-25			
1947.	Double tray		10-15			
1948.	Honey pot with rabbit on side and bee on lid	3.25"h	50-75			
1949.	N/l					
1950.	Bowl		10-15			
1951-1952	N/l					
1953.	Teapot		20-40			
1954.	Floral posy bowl		15-30			
1955.	Flower shape dish	4.5"dia	10-15			
1956.	Wall pocket Budgie, blue	8"h	60-90			
1956.	Wall pocket Budgie, green	8"h	60-90			
1956.	Wall pocket half open fan	5.75"h	20-30			
1956.	Wall pocket Swallow	8"h	80-120			
1957.	Floral posy bowl		15-25			
1958.	Squirrel jug with lip	7.25"h	20-35			
1959.	Squirrel jug with lip	8.5"h	35-50			
1960.	Stork jug	10"h	50-70			
1961.	Spill vase / or holder with duck	3.5"h 3"w	15-25			
1962.	Hollyhock jug	8.5"h	35-45			

Mould No	Description	Size	Price Guide in £'s	Colour	Date Purchased	Price Paid
1963.	Posy vase heart shape with pixie		20-30			
1964.	Posy vase crescent shape	6"l	8-10			
1965.	Posy vase straight	6"l	5-10			
1966.	Posy vase straight	4"l	4-6			
1967.	Posy vase straight	8"l	5-8			
1968.	Dish with handle	5"dia	10-15			
1969.	Mushroom jug gnomes as handle	8.5"h	40-60			
1970.	Jug	5.25"h	15-20			
1971.	Jug	5.25"h	15-20			
1972.	Wall pocket		20-30			
1973.	N/I					
1974.	Jam/honey pot		8-12			
1975.	Box		8-15			
1976.	Ashtray coronation Elizabeth II		25-40			
1977.	N/I					
1978.	Rabbit jug	8.5"h	40-65			
1979.	N/I					
1980.	Honey pot		10-15			
1981.	N/I					
1982.	Fern pot		10-20			
1983.	Fern pot		10-20			
1984.	Fern pot		10-20			
1985.	Jug		12-18			

Mould No	Description	Size	Price Guide in £'s	Colour	Date Purchased	Price Paid
1986.	Jug		12-18			
1987.	Jug		12-18			
1988.	Jug		12-18			
1989.	Jug		12-18			
1990.	Toast rack & butter with dog's head	6.75"l	40-50			
1991.	Basket		10-15			
1992.	Posy round	6"dia	5-10			
1993.	Miniature squirrel jug	3"h	20-30			
1994.	Ashtray		5-15			
1995.	Jug		10-20			
1996.	Basket with dog or other	2"h	20-30			
1997.	Heart shape box with floral lid	4.5"dia	20-35			
1998.	Open barrel		8-12			
1999.	Posy vase		8-10			
2000.	N/I					
2001.	Dish shell with raised flowers		15-20			
2002.	Bowl		10-20			
2003.	Ashtray		5-10			
2004.	Bowl		10-20			
2005.	Ashtray		5-10			
2006.	Floral posy	1.5"h	15-20			
2007.	Jug miniature	2.75"h	20-30			
2008-2018	N/I					

Mould No	Description	Size	Price Guide in £'s	Colour	Date Purchased	Price Paid
2019.	Tray 'Chrys' ware		10-15			
2020.	N/I					
2021.	Tray		10-20			
2022.	Heart shape box with floral lid	3.5"dia	30-40			
2023.	Posy vase straight	7"l	5-10			
2024.	Posy vase as Sealyham dog	7"l 2"h	20-35			
2025.	Posy vase as Spaniel dog	7"l 2"h	20-35			
2026.	N/I					
2027.	Bowl 'Ivyleaf' range Reg No 874069 (1954)	6.25"l	15-20			
2028.	Bowl		10-20			
2029.	Chicken Vase		50-60			
2030.	Basket		12-20			
2031.	Vase 'Chrys' ware	4.5"h	8-12			
2032.	Tray with holder 'Ivyleaf' range Reg No 874070	8"l	15-28			
2033.	Long Posy 'Ivyleaf' range Reg No 874069	7.5"l	10-15			
2034.	N/I					
2035.	Bowl 'Ivyleaf' range Reg No 874069	9.5"l	15-25			
2036.	Jug 'Ivyleaf' range Reg No 874069	8.25"h	25-35			
2037.	Jug 'Ivyleaf' range Reg No 874072	6"h	20-30			
2038.	Tray		8-10			
2039.	Dish with handle 'Ivyleaf' range Reg No 874069	3.5"h	25-35			
2040.	Tray		8-10			
2041.	Bowl		10-12			

Mould No	Description	Size	Price Guide in £'s	Colour	Date Purchased	Price Paid
2042.	Basket		10-15			
2043.	Plant pot 'Ivyleaf' range Reg No 874069	4"h	15-25			
2044.	Vase as above	7"l	15-20			
2045.	Jug 'Ivyleaf' range Reg No 874069	3"h	20-30			
2046.	Honey pot 'Ivyleaf' range Reg No 874069	4.5"h	15-25			
2047.	Plant pot 'Ivyleaf' range Reg No 874069	5"h	20-30			
2048.	Bowl as mushroom		10-20			
2049.	Bowl with gnome	4.25"h	30-50			
2050.	Wall pocket 'Ivyleaf' range Reg No 874069	7.5"h	30-40			
2051.	Old slipper with dog	3.5"h	20-35			
2052.	Wall vase similar to 2050	5"h	20-30			
2053.	N/I					
2054.	Posy Holder with animal	5"dia	30-40			
2055-2059	N/I					
2060.	Old boot	4.25"h	15-25			
2061.	Long vase squirrel handles as 2075	11.5"l	20-35			
2062.	Vase as tree stump with animals	7.25"dia	45-65			
2063.	N/I					
2064.	Leaf shape dish 'Ivyleaf' range Reg No 874069	13"l	15-25			
2065.	N/I					
2066.	Cat in large laced boot		20-35			
2067.	N/I					
2068.	Watercress Dish and stand 'Ivyleaf' Reg No 874069	9.5"l	15-25			

Mould No	Description	Size	Price Guide in £'s	Colour	Date Purchased	Price Paid
2069.	Bowl 'Ivyleaf' range with rabbit or dog	3.75"h	45-65			
2070.	Vase 'Ivyleaf'	6.5"h	10-25			
2070.	Lamp base as above 'Ivyleaf' range	6.5"h	30-40			
2071.	Jug 'Ivyleaf' range	6"h	20-30			
2072.	Jug 'Ivyleaf' range	6"h	20-30			
2073.	Jug 'Ivyleaf' range	6"h	20-30			
2074.	Dish 'Ivyleaf' range	9.75"l	15-28			
2075.	Long vase squirrel handles as 2061	6"l	15-25			
2076.	N/l					
2077.	Jug 'Ivyleaf' range	8.5"h	25-40			
2078.	Jug 'Ivyleaf' range	7.25"h	25-35			
2079.	Wall pocket with seagull	6.25"h	40-60			
2080.	Tray		8-15			
2081.	Vase		10-20			
2082.	Vase		10-20			
2083.	Floral wall pocket double flowers	6.5"h	40-60			
2084.	Floral wall pocket	6"h	40-60			
2085.	Basket		10-20			
2086.	Jug with seagull	6.25"h	55-70			
2087.	Jug 'Chrys' ware	6"h	20-30			
2088.	Cheese dish 'Ivyleaf' range Reg No 874069	3.5"	30-45			
2089.	Candy box round 'Ivyleaf' range as above	2.5"h	15-25			
2090.	Bowl on foot 'Ivyleaf' range	4"h	20-35			

Mould No	Description	Size	Price Guide in £'s	Colour	Date Purchased	Price Paid
2091.	Wall pocket 'Chrys' ware	5.25"h	25-35			
2092.	Wall pocket 'Chrys' ware	9"h	30-50			
2093.	Jug 'Chrys' ware	3"h	15-25			
2094.	Jug 'Chrys' ware	6"h	20-35			
2095.	Jug 'Chrys' ware	7.25"h	20-35			
2096.	Jug 'Chrys' ware	9"h	40-50			
2097.	Bowl 'Chrys' ware	4"h 6"l	8-15			
2098.	Bowl 'Chrys' ware	9.5"l	15-25			
2099.	Pot 'Chrys' ware	4.25"h	15-20			
2100.	Pot 'Chrys' ware	5.25"h	20-30			
2101.	Posy ring 'Chrys' ware	5.75"dia	10-15			
2102.	Posy bar 'Chrys' ware	8"l	10-15			
2103.	Jug 'Chrys' ware	5.75"h	20-30			
2104.	Jug 'Chrys' ware	4.75"h	20-30			
2105.	Jam pot and cover 'Chrys' ware	4"h	15-25			
2106.	Jam pot and cover		10-15			
2107.	Tray		10-15			
2108.	Basket 'Chrys' ware	3.25"h	20-30			
2109.	Basket 'Chrys' ware	4"h	25-35			
2110.	Wall Pocket		20-30			
2111.	Candy box seagull on lid	5"dia	30-40			
2112.	Bowl seagull	9.5"w	40-55			
2113.	Vase oval with seagull	7.5"w	35-45			

Mould No	Description	Size	Price Guide in £'s	Colour	Date Purchased	Price Paid
2114.	Bowl 'Autumn' range		30-40			
2115.	Plant pot 'Autumn' range		30-40			
2116.	Vase 'Autumn' range	7.5"l	30-40			
2117.	Vase		10-20			
2118.	Vase 'Chrys' ware	5.5"h	15-25			
2119.	Basket with seagull	6.5"h	55-70			
2120.	Cat sitting Sim to 1086	5"h	60-85			
2121.	N/I					
2122.	Floral bowl posy	2"h	15-20			
2123.	N/I					
2124.	Vase 'Ivyleaf' Reg No 874069	8.5"h	25-35			
2125.	Vase		10-20			
2126.	N/I					
2127.	Vase plant pot		10-20			
2128.	Floral shell shape dish With seagull or flowers		20-30			
2129.	Plant pot 'Rope Range'	4.75"h	10-20			
2130.	Vase 'Rope Range'	5.5"h	10-15			
2131.	Oval posy 'Rope Range'	8"l	8-10			
2132.	Oval vase 'Rope Range'	9"l	8-10			
2133.	Floral Posy		15-25			
2134.	Bowl bow shape	6"l	15-25			
2135.	Bowl		20-30			
2136.	Vase	5.5"h	8-12			

Mould No	Description	Size	Price Guide in £'s	Colour	Date Purchased	Price Paid
2137.	Vase	8"h	15-20			
2138.	Low dish on feet	11.5"l	10-15			
2139.	Vase	8.25"h	8-10			
2140.	Wall pocket plain shield shape	8"h	15-25			
2141.	Bowl		5-15			
2142.	Low dish	7.5"l	5-8			
2143.	Bowl		5-15			
2144.	Vase	11"h	15-25			
2145.	Bowl		5-15			
2146.	Bowl		5-15			
2147.	Vase on feet	8"h	10-15			
2148.	Bowl		15-25			
2149.	N/I					
2150.	Plant pot 'Rope Range'	6.75"dia	10-20			
2151.	Wall pocket 'Rope Range'	8.5"h	15-20			
2152.	Vase 'Autumn' range		20-35			
2153.	Bowl		5-15			
2154.	Wall pocket floral bow		20-35			
2155.	Vase		10-20			
2156.	Wall pocket 'Autumn' range		25-35			
2157.	N/I					
2158.	Pixie sitting on upturned mushroom	3.25"h	45-60			
2159.	Vase 'Autumn' range	14"h	30-45			

Mould No	Description	Size	Price Guide in £'s	Colour	Date Purchased	Price Paid
2160.	Plant pot holder 'Rope Range'	6"h	10-15			
2161.	Vase 'Rope Range'	3"h	5-8			
2162.	Vase 'Rope Range'	6"h	8-10			
2163.	Vase 'Rope Range'	7"h	8-12			
2164.	Vase		5-20			
2165.	Miniature thistle jug	2.5"h	15-20			
2166.	Bowl to go with above	2.5"h	8-10			
2167.	Plant pot	7"l	8-12			
2168.	Candlestick thistle shape	1.75"h	10-15			
2169.	Tray		5-15			
2170.	Tray		5-15			
2171.	Plant pot holder 'Raphique' range		10-15			
2172.	Jam Pot 'Raphique' range	4.5"h	8-12			
2173.	Vase	5"h	5-10			
2174.	Candlestick Similar to 1352		20-35			
2175.	Vase		5-20			
2176.	Vase 'Raphique' range		5-20			
2177.	Jam/honey pot 'Raphique' range	4.5"h	8-12			
2178.	Long posy 'Raphique' range	8.25"l	5-10			
2179.	Butter dish 'Raphique' range	5.75"l	10-15			
2180.	Vase 'Raphique' range		5-20			
2181.	Wall pocket 'Raphique' range	8.75"h	20-30			
2182.	Bowl 'Raphique' range		10-15			

Mould No	Description	Size	Price Guide in £'s	Colour	Date Purchased	Price Paid
2183.	Bowl		10-15			
2184.	Salt, pepper, mustard and tray 'Raphique' range		20-25			
2185.	Small jug 'Raphique' range		5-10			
2186.	Salt and pepper		10-15			
2187.	Long posy vase 'Rope Range'	15"l	8-15			
2188.	Teapot 'Raphique' range		20-30			
2189.	Vase 'Raphique' range		5-20			
2190.	Bowl small 'Raphique' range		5-10			
2191.	Bowl 'Raphique' range		10-20			
2192.	Vase 'Raphique' range		10-20			
2193.	Wall pocket		20-30			
2194.	Vase		5-20			
2195.	Wall pocket		20-30			
2196.	Cheese dish		15-25			
2197.	Butter dish		10-15			
2198.	Vase 'Raphique' range	5.25"h	5-20			
2199.	Vase 'Raphique' range		5-20			
2200.	Small bowl		8-10			
2201.	Small jug		8-10			
2202.	Tray		5-10			
2203.	Teapot		20-30			
2204.	Pot		8-12			
2205.	Vase upright fish		20-30			

Mould No	Description	Size	Price Guide in £'s	Colour	Date Purchased	Price Paid
2206.	Candle holder 'Blackberry' range		10-15			
2207.	N/I					
2208.	Floral wall pocket	7"h	50-70			
2209.	Plant pot holder 'Cactus' range		15-20			
2210.	Jug		5-15			
2211.	Toast rack		15-20			
2212.	Vase 'Lace' range	5.25"h	5-20			
2213.	Bowl 'Raphique' range	7"l	5-15			
2214.	Tray		5-15			
2215.	Posy trough		5-10			
2216.	Bowl		5-15			
2217.	Vase		5-15			
2218.	Vase trumpet shape		15-20			
2219.	Vase		5-20			
2220.	Vase impressed circles	6.5"h	15-20			
2221.	Lamp		15-25			
2222.	Wall pocket		15-30			
2223.	Dish 'Lace' range	5.25"dia	8-12			
2224.	Vase 'Oak Wood' range	5"h	10-25			
2225.	Dish	5.25l	8-12			
2226.	Honey pot 'Cactus' range		10-15			
2227.	Vase 'Rope' range	12"l	15-20			
2228.	Plant pot impressed circles		15-20			

Mould No	Description	Size	Price Guide in £'s	Colour	Date Purchased	Price Paid
2229.	Plant pot impressed circles		15-20			
2230.	Pot small round	3.5"h	5-10			
2231.	Vase		5-15			
2232.	Vase		5-15			
2233.	Vase		5-15			
2234.	N/I					
2235.	Wall pocket	7"h	8-12			
2236.	Bowl circles	9.5"l	15-20			
2237.	Vase		5-15			
2238.	Vase long 'Rope' range	8"l	8-10			
2239.	Plant pot Snow drop	4.75"h	5-15			
2240.	Bowl		5-15			
2241.	N/I					
2242.	Bowl		5-15			
2243.	Vase		5-15			
2244.	Jam/honey pot 'Lace' range	1.75"h	10-15			
2245.	Dish 'Cactus' range	4.25"l	15-20			
2246.	Vase 'Cactus' range	6"h	20-30			
2247.	Wall pocket 'Cactus' range	8.5"h	30-45			
2248.	Plant pot 'Cactus' range	5"h	15-25			
2249.	Bowl 'Cactus' range	4.5"h 6.5"l	15-25			
2250.	Vase		5-15			
2251.	Vase 'Cactus' range		20-30			

Mould No	Description	Size	Price Guide in £'s	Colour	Date Purchased	Price Paid
2252.	Vase 'Cactus' range	8"h	25-35			
2253.	Pot		5-20			
2254.	Vase 'Cactus' range	7"h	25-35			
2255.	Vase 'Lace' range	6"h	10-20			
2256.	Bowl		5-20			
2257.	Bowl 'Chrys' range	4.25"h	10-20			
2258.	Vase		5-20			
2259.	Bowl 'Shell' range	12"l	20-30			
2260.	Vase 'Floral' range		15-25			
2261.	Dish	6.5"dia	5-10			
2262.	Wall pocket 'Cactus' range	6.5"h	30-40			
2263.	Wall pocket 'Cactus' range	5.25"h	30-40			
2264.	Vase two handles 'Rope Range'	14"l	15-20			
2265.	Vase 'Rope' range	5"h	8-12			
2266.	Vase 'Rope' range	8"h	10-15			
2267.	Vase 'Floral' range	5.25"h	15-25			
2268.	Vase 'Lace' range	6.75"h	10-20			
2269.	Wall pocket 'Lace' range	8.75"h	20-30			
2270.	Plant pot holder 'Lace' range	4.75"h	8-12			
2271.	Jam/Honey pot 'Lace' range	3.75"h	8-12			
2272.	Vase		5-15			
2273.	Tray 'Lace' range	12.5"l	15-25			
2274.	Wall pocket 'Lace' range	7.25"h	20-30			

Mould No	Description	Size	Price Guide in £'s	Colour	Date Purchased	Price Paid
2275.	Log posy vase with pixie	5"l	15-35			
2276.	Posy basket with pixie	5"l	10-35			
2277.	Posy vase watering can with gnome	3"h	10-35			
2278.	Flower pot posy vase with pixie	3"h	15-40			
2279.	Bowl		5-15			
2280.	Vase 'Rope Range'	12"l	10-18			
2281.	Vase	7"h	10-15			
2282.	Vase	7"h	10-15			
2283.	N/I					
2284.	Posy 'Lace' range	7.5"dia	5-8			
2285.	Tray		5-10			
2286.	Vase with ridges similar to 1758	5-6"h	10-20			
2287.	Vase		5-15			
2288.	Vase	7"h	10-15			
2289.	Bowl square embossed with pixie	5.5"l	35-45			
2290.	Bowl 'Lace' range	6"dia	10-20			
2291.	Vase		5-15			
2292.	N/I					
2293.	Wall pocket 'Cactus' range		20-30			
2294.	Flower pot 'Lace' range	5.5"h	15-20			
2295.	Plant holder half acorn with pixie	7"dia	15-30			
2296.	Vase 'Cactus' range		5-15			
2297.	Posy vase 'Lace' range		5-15			

Mould No	Description	Size	Price Guide in £'s	Colour	Date Purchased	Price Paid
2298.	Salt, pepper & mustard 'Lace' range		15-25			
2299.	Dish 'Lace' range	11"dia	5-15			
2300.	Vase 'Lace' range	12"w	5-15			
2301.	Plant pot 'Lace' range	9.75"dia	5-15			
2302.	Vase		5-15			
2303.	Vase 'Cactus' range		15-30			
2304.	Vase		5-15			
2305.	Vase 'Cactus' range	7.5"h	20-30			
2306.	Wall pocket 'Cactus' range		20-30			
2307.	Acorn bowl		5-15			
2308.	Vase 'Cactus' range		15-25			
2309.	Posy vase 'Lace' range	4.5"dia	5-10			
2310.	Wall pocket		20-30			
2311.	Floral posy	2.5"h 4"l	10-15			
2312.	Vase 'Floral Range'	5"h	15-25			
2313.	Holder on stand	4.75"h	20-30			
2314.	Tree vase 'Privet' range	4.75"h	20-30			
2315.	Dish 'Floral Range'	5"l	5-10			
2316.	Bowl 'Floral Range'		15-20			
2317.	Bowl 'Floral Range'		15-20			
2318.	Bowl 'Floral Range'		15-20			
2319.	Tray 'Nuleef' range	11.25"l	15-20			
2320.	Bowl 'Rope Range'	7"dia	10-15			

Mould No	Description	Size	Price Guide in £'s	Colour	Date Purchased	Price Paid
2321.	Vase 'Hyacinth' range	7"h	8-15			
2322.	Wall pocket		20-30			
2323.	Candleholder 'Lace' range	2.5"h	5-10			
2324.	N/I					
2325.	Small dish		5-10			
2326.	Dish similar to 2325	7.25"l	5-10			
2327.	Cheese dish 'Lace' range		15-25			
2328.	Vase swan shape		5-15			
2329.	Vase	5"h	8-12			
2330.	Acorn Vase embossed leaves		20-30			
2331.	Dog Boxer sitting	5.25"h	70-100			
2332.	Baby's bootee	3.25"h	15-25			
2333.	Bowl/vase 'Nuleef' range	6.5"h	10-20			
2334.	Vase 'Nuleef' range	5. 5"h	10-18			
2335.	Jam/honey pot 'Nuleef' range	5.25"h	15-20			
2336.	Bonbon dish 'Nuleef' range		15-20			
2337.	Vase	10.25"h	10-20			
2338.	Vase		5-15			
2339.	Bowl/planter embossed mushrooms & pixie	9"dia	35-55			
2340.	Vase 'Lace' range	8.25"w	5-15			
2341.	Jug 'Nuleef' range	8"h	25-35			
2342.	Mug 'Nuleef' range	4.5"h	5-10			
2343.	Beer Mug raised horses head	4.5"h	10-20			

Mould No	Description	Size	Price Guide in £'s	Colour	Date Purchased	Price Paid
2344.	Beer Mug		10-20			
2345.	Vase 'Plume' range	7"h	15-20			
2346.	Bowl/planter embossed mushrooms & pixie	7. 5"dia	35-45			
2347.	Sweet dish 'Lace' range	5.25"w	15-20			
2348.	Toastrack 'Nuleef' range		15-20			
2349.	3 pce condiment set on tray 'Nuleef' range		20-35			
2350.	N/I					
2351.	Jug 'Nuleef' range 3 sizes	from 4.5"h	10-30			
2352.	Vase	6"h	10-18			
2353.	Watercress dish and stand 'Nuleef' range	11.5"l	20-35			
2354.	Double dish 'Nuleef' range		8-15			
2355.	Dish 'Nuleef' range	8.25"l	5-10			
2356.	Butter dish 'Nuleef' range		25-35			
2357.	Cheese dish 'Nuleef' range		30-40			
2358.	Triple dish 'Nuleef' range		20-30			
2359.	Dish 'Nuleef' range	12"l	15-20			
2360.	Plant pot holder 'Nuleef' range		20-25			
2361.	Bowl/vase 'Nuleef' range		8-15			
2362.	Small bowl 'Nuleef' range	4"dia	5-10			
2363.	Small jug 'Nuleef' range		15-20			
2364.	Posy vase long 'Nuleef' range		8-12			
2365.	Bowl		5-10			
2366.	Wall pocket 'Nuleef' range		20-30			

Mould No	Description	Size	Price Guide in £'s	Colour	Date Purchased	Price Paid
2367.	Round bowl large 'Nuleef' range		25-35			
2368.	Vase 'Nuleef' range	6"h	15-25			
2369.	Butter dish		10-15			
2370.	Tray		5-10			
2371.	Bowl small		5-10			
2372.	Wall pocket 'Lily' range		45-65			
2373.	Floral jug		20-30			
2374.	N/I					
2375.	Beer mug raised dog head	4.5"h	10-15			
2376.	Beer mug raised fox head	4.5"h	10-15			
2377.	N/I					
2378.	Pot bucket shape	4.75"h	8-10			
2379.	Vase two handles oval	8"l	8-12			
2380.	Bowl		5-15			
2381.	Bowl		5-15			
2382.	Plant pot embossed leaves		10-18			
2383.	Vase		5-15			
2384.	Vase		5-15			
2385.	Long posy vase 'Plume' range		8-10			
2386.	Wall pocket 'Plume' range		20-30			
2387.	Bowl		5-15			
2388.	Pot bucket shape		20-30			
2389.	Plant pot 'Nuleef' range	6.25"h	15-20			

Mould No	Description	Size	Price Guide in £'s	Colour	Date Purchased	Price Paid
2390.	Vase		5-15			
2391.	Vase		5-18			
2392.	Vase		5-18			
2393.	Bowl		5-18			
2394.	Beer mug plain		5-10			
2395.	Beer mug plain		5-10			
2396.	Mother duck with hat		150-190			
2397.	Baby duck with knitted hat	2.25"h	40-60			
2398.	Baby duck with wings showing	2.25"h	40-60			
2399.	Bowl	6"l	5-15			
2400.	Dish 'Plume' range	11.5"l	5-20			
2401.	Vase 'Plume' range	3.5"h 6.25"l	10-15			
2402.	Plant pot holder 'Plume' range		10-18			
2403.	Cheese dish 'Plume' range		15-25			
2404.	Vase 'Plume' range	6.25"h	8-15			
2405.	Bowl 'Plume' range	13"l	8-15			
2406.	Vase with two handles 'Plume' range	8.5"l	10-18			
2407.	Vase 'Plume' range		15-20			
2408.	Vase 'Plume' range	5.5"h	10-18			
2409.	Salt, pepper, mustard with tray 'Plume' range		20-30			
2410.	Jam/honey pot 'Plume' range		8-15			
2411.	Butter dish 'Plume' range		15-20			
2412.	N/I					

Mould No	Description	Size	Price Guide in £'s	Colour	Date Purchased	Price Paid
2413.	N/I					
2414.	Bowl		5-20			
2415.	Bowl		5-20			
2416.	Bowl		5-20			
2417.	Bowl		5-20			
2418.	Vase		5-20			
2419.	Vase 'Nuleef' range		10-18			
2420.	Vase 'Nuleef' range	8.25"h	5-20			
2421.	Dog sitting with barrel on neck	4.75"h	40-55			
2422.	Dog - begging scottie used for 'add ons'	2"h	30-40			
2423.	N/I					
2424.	Ashtray dog's head and tail	5.5"l	15-25			
2425.	Chimney and with the following	4"h	30-45			
	Cat	4"h	30-45			
	Owl	4"h	30-45			
	Stork	4"h	30-45			
2426.	N/I					
2427.	Hippo Not issued separately					
2428.	Giraffe Not issued separately					
2429.	Elephant Not issued separately					
2430.	Vase in shape of palm and with the following	4"h	30-50			
	Giraffe		30-50			
	Hippo	4"h	30-50			
	Elephant	4"h	30-50			
2431.	Ashtray dog's head and tail	5.5"l	15-22			

Mould No	Description	Size	Price Guide in £'s	Colour	Date Purchased	Price Paid
2432.	Beer mug horse		10-15			
2433.	Beer mug hounds head		10-15			
2434.	Tankard		10-15			
2435.	Beer mug horse		10-15			
2436.	Beer mug		10-15			
2437.	Beer mug fox		10-15			
2438.	Ashtray Pekinese head and tail	5.75"l	15-22			
2439.	Vase 'Nautilus' range	6"h	10-15			
2440.	Vase 'Nautilus' range	6.5"h	10-15			
2441.	Vase 'Nautilus' range	10"h	15-25			
2442.	Vase		5-15			
2443.	Owl not issued separately					
2444.	Stork not issued separately					
2445.	Vase		5-18			
2446.	Vase	6"h	5-18			
2447.	Vase	6"h	5-18			
2448.	Vase	6.25"h	5-18			
2449.	Vase 'Nautilus' range	8"h	15-20			
2450.	Pot Six sizes		5-18			
2451.	Toothache dog	11"h	280-350			
2452.	Vase 'Hyacinth' range	9.25"h	8-15			
2453.	Vase 'Hyacinth' range	11.25"h	10-20			
2454.	Bowl		5-15			

Mould No	Description	Size	Price Guide in £'s	Colour	Date Purchased	Price Paid
2455.	Toothache dog	8.25"h	120-150			
2456.	Vase 'Hyacinth' range	10"h	15-20			
2457.	Vase squirrel & large tail	5.75"h	20-30			
2458.	Bowl		5-15			
2459.	Vase double squirrel & tails	5.75"h	20-30			
2460.	Vase several shapes same number		15-20			
2461.	Plant pot holder 'Jewel' range	4.75"h	15-20			
2462.	N/I					
2463.	Vase classical	8.25"h	10-18			
2464.	Vase		5-15			
2465.	Centre piece bowl 'Moselle' range cherub base	9"h	30-65			
2466.	Water wheel		10-15			
2467.	Vase	7"l	8-15			
2468.	Vase crescent squirrel and tail	5.75"l	15-20			
2469.	N/I					
2470.	N/I					
2471.	N/I					
2472.	Vase Lilac sprays	5"h	10-15			
2473.	Dog small long hair	4"h	40-70			
2474.	Bowl on foot 'Moselle' range	10.5"l	25-35			
2475.	Flower pot 'Laronde' range	5.5"h	8-15			
2476.	Vase embossed lilac sprays	5"h	10-15			
2477.	Dog		20-40			

Mould No	Description	Size	Price Guide in £'s	Colour	Date Purchased	Price Paid
2478.	Long vase 'Hyacinth' range	14.25"l	10-15			
2479.	Bowl		10-15			
2480.	Wall pocket		20-30			
2481.	Bowl		5-15			
2482.	Bowl oval 'Hyacinth' range	6.75"l	8-10			
2483.	Plant pot holder 'Hyacinth' range	5"h	10-15			
2484.	Vase with two handles 'Hyacinth' range	13"l	18-25			
2485.	Bowl oval 'Hyacinth' range	10.5"l	10-20			
2486.	Long posy vase 'Hyacinth' range	8"l	5-8			
2487.	Wall pocket 'Hyacinth' range	9"h	20-30			
2488.	Vase with two handles 'Hyacinth' range	8.25"l	10-15			
2489.	Plant pot holder 'Hyacinth' range	6"h	15-25			
2490.	N/I					
2491.	Bowl Lilac sprays		15-20			
2492.	N/I					
2493.	Dog St Bernard on all fours	4.5"h	25-40			
2494.	Vase classical	6.25"h	4-6			
2495.	Vase classical	10.25"h	12-20			
2496.	N/I					
2497.	Dog Spaniel on all fours	4.25"h	30-40			
2498.	Floral bowl 7 flowers		10-25			
2499.	Floral bowl 10 flowers		15-30			
2500.	Floral bowl 12 flowers		18-35			

Mould No	Description	Size	Price Guide in £'s	Colour	Date Purchased	Price Paid
2501.	Tray toadstool with dog		30-45			
2502.	Dog Collie on all fours	5.5"h	25-40			
2503.	Dog Terrier on all fours	4"h	25-40			
2504.	Dog Boston Terrier	4.5"h	25-40			
2505.	Vase deco as 1346	15"h	25-45			
2506.	Vase		5-18			
2507.	Bowl squirrel and tail	5.75"l	20-38			
2508.	N/I					
2509.	Barrel with animals		20-35			
2510.	Floral posy bowl 4-5 flowers		10-20			
2511.	Tray		5-12			
2512.	Plant pot holder Squirrels	7.5"dia	20-30			
2513.	Bowl with leaves draped over side	7.25"dia	20-30			
2514.	Vase classical shape	7.25"h	10-18			
2515.	Vase		5-20			
2516.	Ashtray With Beagle	6.5"dia	8-10			
2517.	Ashtray fox	6.5"dia	8-10			
2518.	Ashtray horse	6.5"dia	8-10			
2519.	Leaf for 2513 not issued separately					
2420.	Leaf for 2513 not issued separately					
2521.	Bookends horse head	4.25"h	50-90			
2522.	Bookends fish with wave	3.75"h	80-130			
2523.	Squirrel		15-25			

Mould No	Description	Size	Price Guide in £'s	Colour	Date Purchased	Price Paid
2524.	Dog Bloodhound sitting	5"h	65-105			
2525.	Floral posy bowl with 14 flowers		20-30			
2526.	Bowl 'Duck family'	8"dia	50-80			
2527.	Pot		5-15			
2528.	Dog Setter on all fours	4.75"h	25-35			
2529.	Squirrel		15-25			
2530.	N/I					
2531.	Long vase		8-10			
2532.	N/I					
2533.	Ashtray round		8-10			
2534.	N/I					
2535.	Bowl with 3 flowers	3.5"h	10-20			
2536.	Dog		30-50			
2537.	Dog sitting Greyhound	7.5"l	25-35			
2538.	Dog Airedale on all fours	5"h	25-35			
2539.	N/I					
2540.	Dog cairn terrier	4"l	30-50			
2541.	Bowl		5-15			
2542.	Bowl		5-15			
2543.	Vase		5-18			
2544.	Vase		5-18			
2545.	Dog smooth haired Terrier		25-35			
2546.	Plant pot holder 'Laronde' range	5.5"h	10-15			

Mould No	Description	Size	Price Guide in £'s	Colour	Date Purchased	Price Paid
2547.	Posy 'Bamboo' range	3.75"h	5-10			
2548.	Vase 'Moselle' range		20-40			
2549.	Cat caricature	5"h	60-95			
2550.	Vase		5-18			
2551.	Plant pot holder 'Jewel' range	5.5"h	10-15			
2552.	Bookends		20-25			
2553.	Vase		5-18			
2554.	Jug		10-15			
2555.	Jam/honey pot 'Kitchen' range	4.5"h	15-25			
2556.	Small bowl 'Kitchen' range	2.25"h	8-10			
2557.	Small jug		8-10			
2558.	Plant pot holder		10-15			
2559.	Plant pot 'Jewel' range	4"h	8-15			
2560.	Shoe		10-20			
2561.	N/I					
2562.	Comport 'Moselle' range cherub base	7.75"h	35-55			
2563.	Tray		5-12			
2564.	Vase 'Moselle' range on foot	8.5"h	15-25			
2565.	Vase urn shape 'Heirlooms' range		10-20			
2566.	Cake plate 'Moselle' range on foot	12"dia	20-30			
2567.	Flower pot holder 'Laronde' range	4.25"h	8-10			
2568.	Flower pot holder 'Laronde' range	4.75"h	8-10			
2569.	Bowl Gondola similar to 2601,2862		20-30			

Mould No	Description	Size	Price Guide in £'s	Colour	Date Purchased	Price Paid
2570.	Mug		5-10			
2571.	Teapot		20-30			
2572.	Seal	7.5"	65-85			
2573.	Match holder		8-10			
2574.	Bulldog		55-90			
2575.	Cheese dish		15-20			
2576.	Mustard pot & lid Embossed 'Kitchen' range	2.5"h	10-15			
2577.	Jug large 'Kitchen' range	7.25"h	15-25			
2578.	Bowl		5-15			
2579.	Cat		45-85			
2580.	Deer lying	5.25"h 5.5"l	45-85			
2581.	Jug		5-15			
2582.	Jug		5-15			
2583.	Jug		5-15			
2584.	Howling dog	7.5"h	60-120			
2585.	Butter dish		10-15			
2586.	Kitchen jar with lid	5.5"h	10-15			
2587.	Kitchen jar		10-15			
2588.	Kitchen jar		10-15			
2589.	Sugar sifter		10-15			
2590.	Jug		5-15			
2591.	Watercress dish and stand		15-25			
2592.	Large bowl		15-25			

Mould No	Description	Size	Price Guide in £'s	Colour	Date Purchased	Price Paid
2593.	Wall pocket Squirrel and tail	8"h	25-40			
2594.	Pig standing	7"l 3.5"h	45-75			
2595.	Dog Dachshund	4"h 6.5"l	75-90			
2596.	N/I					
2597.	Bootee	2.25"h 3.25"l	10-15			
2598.	Long vase Squirrel either end	14"l	20-35			
2599.	Vase		5-18			
2600.	Plant pot holder two squirrels inset	10"dia	24-28			
2601.	Bowl similar to 2569,2862 as Gondola	6.5"l	30-45			
2601.	Bowl as Gondola filled with flowers		40-60			
2602.	Dish 'Laronde' range		8-12			
2603.	Beer mug Moulin de Lecq Inn		15-20			
2604.	Teapot large		35-45			
2605.	Teapot small 'Kitchen' range	5"h	20-30			
2606.	Bowl		5-15			
2607.	Wall pocket 'Laronde' range	6.25"h	10-18			
2608.	Long vase 'Laronde' range	7.75"l	5-10			
2609.	Vase 'Laronde' range	7"h	10-15			
2610.	Bowl 'Laronde' range	6.5"l	5-8			
2611.	Basket 'Laronde' range	7.5"h 7.75l	10-15			
2612.	Salt, pepper & mustard 'Laronde' range		15-25			
2613.	Bowl 'Laronde' range	14"l	8-10			
2614.	Vase 'Laronde' range	10.5"l	8-12			

Mould No	Description	Size	Price Guide in £'s	Colour	Date Purchased	Price Paid
2615.	Jam/honey pot 'Laronde' range	5"h	5-10			
2616.	Vase 'Laronde' range	10"h	12-20			
2617.	Vase 'Laronde' range	8"h	10-15			
2618.	Vase 'Laronde' range	6"h	8-12			
2619.	Cheese dish 'Laronde' range	7.5"l	10-20			
2620.	Dish 'Laronde' range	12.5"l	8-12			
2621.	Dish 'Laronde' range	11.25"d	8-12			
2622.	Bowl		8-12			
2623.	Dog Spaniel		45-85			
2624.	N/I					
2625.	Bowl centre piece 'Moselle' range two cherubs	14"l	45-80			
2626.	Vase 'Moselle' range horn & cherub	8.75"h	30-45			
2627.	Bottle holder		5-12			
2628.	N/I					
2629.	Bowl		5-15			
2630.	Bowl		15-25			
2631.	Vase		5-18			
2632.	Vase		5-18			
2632.	Vase with Bird Starling		25-40			
2633.	Cruet novelty set Laurel & Hardy		45-85			
2634.	Triple dish 'Laronde' range	10.5"d	10-15			
2635.	N/I					
2636.	Bowl 'Laronde' range	11"dia	12-18			

Mould No	Description	Size	Price Guide in £'s	Colour	Date Purchased	Price Paid
2637.	N/I					
2638.	Bowl 'Laronde' range	9. 5"l	5-15			
2639.	Vase		5-15			
2640.	N/I					
2641.	N/I					
2642.	Beer mug horse		10-20			
2643.	Vase	4.5"h	5-15			
2644.	N/I					
2645.	Vase 'Ivyleaf' range	10"h	25-35			
2646.	Vase 'Ivyleaf' range	7.5"h	20-30			
2647.	Long vase 'Ivyleaf' range	15"l	15-20			
2648.	Vase/ashtray 'Ivyleaf' range low round	7"dia	10-15			
2649.	Vase 'Ivyleaf' range	12"l	15-25			
2650.	N/I					
2651.	Vase 'Ivyleaf' range	7"h 10"l	15-20			
2652.	Vase 'Ivyleaf' range	8.25"h	20-30			
2653.	Vase 'Ivyleaf' range	6.25"h	20-30			
2654.	N/I					
2655.	Vase with various animals: Dog	5"h	25-35			
	Lamb	5"h	25-35			
	Bear	5"h	25-35			
2656.	Vase with various animals: Dog	5"h	25-35			
	Lamb	5"h	25-35			
	Bear	5"h	25-35			

Mould No	Description	Size	Price Guide in £'s	Colour	Date Purchased	Price Paid
2657.	N/I					
2658.	Vase with various animals: Dog	5"h	25-35			
	Lamb	5"h	25-35			
	Bear	5"h	25-35			
2659.	Vase		5-18			
2660.	Vase with various comic dogs: Tennis dog	5"h	30-40			
	City dog	5"h	30-40			
	French poodle	5"h	30-40			
2661.	Crescent vase 'Ivy' range	1.25"h 6.5"l	5-10			
2662.	N/I					
2663.	Plate		5-12			
2664.	N/I					
2665.	N/I					
2666.	N/I					
2667.	Fawn not issued separately					
2668.	Lamb not issued separately					
2669.	City dog for 2660 not issued separately					
2670.	French poodle for 2660 not issued separately					
2671.	Tennis dog for 2660 not issued separately					
2672.	Dog Clothed with spade	2.75"h	60-80			
2673.	Bowl		5-15			
2674.	N/I					
2675.	Dog Old English Sheepdog	5"h	25-35			
2676.	Leaves Vase	7.752h	5-20			

Mould No	Description	Size	Price Guide in £'s	Colour	Date Purchased	Price Paid
2677.	N/I					
2678.	Vase on four feet	10.5"l	20-25			
2679.	Dog small Scottie	3.5"h	25-35			
2680.	Vase with handle		10-20			
2681.	Blacksmith's anvil		15-25			
2682.	N/I					
2683.	Vase 'Moselle' range cherub & shell	5.5"l	15-25			
2684.	Tray two handles	7.5"l	10-15			
2685.	Luggage trunk		15-25			
2686.	Ashtray	2.25"h 6.25"d	10-20			
2687.	Rabbit and skis	4.5"h 4"l	80-135			
2688.	Rabbit and skis	5.75"h 5.5"l	80-150			
2689.	Rabbit and skis	4.25"h 4"l	75-120			
2690.	Bowl embossed houses	3.5"h 6"d	20-30			
2691.	Bowl embossed houses		20-30			
2692.	Vase		5-18			
2693.	Dog playing tennis tooth brush holder/jug		25-35			
2694.	Vase	6"h	8-12			
2695.	Vase	6"h	8-15			
2696.	Bowl on stand	7.5"l	15-20			
2697.	N/I					
2698.	N/I					
2699.	Vase swan	7.25"l	20-25			

Mould No	Description	Size	Price Guide in £'s	Colour	Date Purchased	Price Paid
2700.	N/I					
2701.	Bowl		5-15			
2702.	N/I					
2703.	Lemon juicer		10-12			
2704.	Plant pot holder	2"h	10-20			
2705.	Vase 'Jewel' range	5.5"h 12.25"l	8-15			
2706.	Vase 'Jewel' range	8"h 6"l	10-20			
2707.	Bowl 'Jewel' range	15"l	10-20			
2708.	Bowl/vase 'Jewel' range	4.5"h 7.5"d	5-15			
2709.	Vase 'Jewel' range	7.25"l	10-20			
2710.	Vase two handles 'Jewel' range	10.5"l	10-20			
2711.	Posy vase 'Jewel' range	8"l	8-10			
2712.	Vase 'Jewel' range	10"h 7.25"l	10-20			
2713.	Vase 'Jewel' range	6"h	8-15			
2714.	Plant pot holder	7.25"h	10-15			
2715.	N/I					
2716.	N/I					
2717.	N/I					
2718.	Twin vase 'Bamboo' range		10-15			
2719.	N/I					
2720.	Wall pocket	9.5"h	20-30			
2721.	Egg separator		10-20			
2722.	Cat flat sitting		55-95			

Mould No	Description	Size	Price Guide in £'s	Colour	Date Purchased	Price Paid
2723.	Bottle holder		8-10			
2724.	Vase		5-20			
2724	Character jug 'Abraham Lincoln'		50-75			
2725.	Tray		10-15			
2726.	Watercress dish and stand		15-25			
2727.	Vase with swan	9.25"l	25-35			
2728.	N/I					
2729.	Bowl small 'Moselle' range with cherub	5.5"l	15-25			
2730.	Dog with spade toothbrush holder/jug		30-50			
2731.	Poodle with umbrella toothbrush holder/jug		30-50			
2732.	Vase 'Bamboo' range	7"h	10-15			
2733.	Bowl		5-15			
2734.	Bowl		5-15			
2735.	Bowl		5-15			
2736.	Figure of boy		60-75			
2737.	Cherub		35-55			
2738.	Monkey jug similar to 1190 & 2807		30-40			
2739.	Vase with two handles	20"l	15-20			
2740.	Bowl 'Bamboo' range	11"l	10-15			
2741.	Wall pocket 'Bamboo' range three sticks	8.5"h	20-25			
2742.	Flower pot holder 'Bamboo' range	4.75"h	10-18			
2743.	Vase 'Bamboo' range crossed pair	8.25"h	15-30			
2744.	Plant pot holder 'Bamboo' range	14.25"l	10-18			

Mould No	Description	Size	Price Guide in £'s	Colour	Date Purchased	Price Paid
2745.	Posy 'Bamboo' range	8.5"l	8-10			
2746.	Vase 'Bamboo' range	9"l	5-15			
2747.	Plant pot holder 'Bamboo' range	5.5"h	10-18			
2748.	Double vase 'Bamboo' range	6"h	10-15			
2749.	Long vase 'Bamboo' range	6.25"l	5-10			
2750.	Long vase 'Bamboo' range	8.5"l	8-12			
2751.	Vase 'Bamboo' range	8"h	5-18			
2752.	Vase 'Bamboo' range	7.5"h	5-18			
2753.	Vase 'Bamboo' range	10"h	10-20			
2754.	Vase 'Bamboo' range	6"h	5-18			
2755.	N/I					
2756.	Cat flat		45-55			
2757.	Seal flat		45-55			
2758.	Owl flat		45-55			
2759.	Dog flat howling		45-55			
2760.	Dog flat		45-55			
2761.	Cow flat		45-55			
2762.	Dog flat Dachshund		45-55			
2763.	Egg cup		5-10			
2764.	Dog flat		45-55			
2765.	N/I					
2766.	Vase 'Bamboo' range low round	6.25"dia	8-12			
2767.	'L' shape posy 'Bamboo' range		5-10			

Mould No	Description	Size	Price Guide in £'s	Colour	Date Purchased	Price Paid
2768.	Bowl on foot	8"dia	10-20			
2769.	Pot		6-15			
2770.	Vase ribbed 'Tropique' range	8.25"h	5-18			
2771.	Wall pocket		20-30			
2772.	Vase		5-18			
2773.	Vase 'Trellis' range	8.5"h 5.5"d	10-15			
2774.	Fan shape vase	5.5"h 10.5"l	10-20			
2775.	Wall pocket		20-30			
2776.	Vase		5-18			
2777.	Vase 'Tropique' range	6.25"h	5-18			
2778.	N/I					
2779.	Vase		5-18			
2780.	Fan shape vase	7"w	10-20			
2781.	Vase		5-15			
2782.	Swan		10-20			
2783.	Posy vase 'Moselle' range with cherub	5.5"l	15-25			
2784.	Bowl embossed basket weave	6"l	8-15			
2785.	Plant pot holder 'Autumn Chintz' range	5.5"h	10-15			
2786.	Vase	7.5"h 13"l	5-18			
2787.	Bowl 'Bamboo' range	10"l	15-25			
2788.	Basket 'Bamboo' range	8.25"h	5-15			
2789.	Cot		10-18			
2790.	Plant pot holder 'Autumn Chintz' range	4.75"h	10-15			

Mould No	Description	Size	Price Guide in £'s	Colour	Date Purchased	Price Paid
2791.	Vase		5-18			
2792.	Vase	6.25"h	5-18			
2793.	Posy vase		5-10			
2794.	Cat flat Sitting small		50-90			
2795.	Cat flat sitting	6.5"h 4.5"w	80-110			
2796.	Plant pot holder	4.25"h	10-15			
2797.	Dog		35-45			
2798.	Posy vase with owl on tree	2.75"h	25-40			
2799.	Posy vase gnome on bamboo	3"h	25-35			
2800.	Posy vase fox on pine cone	3"h	25-45			
2801.	Vase 'Trellis' range	5.5"h	8-12			
2802.	Plant pot 'Trellis' range	4.5"h	8-12			
2803.	Vase	6"h	5-20			
2804.	Bowl	7.5"h	5-15			
2805.	Bowl		5-20			
2806.	Vase round	6.25"h	10-15			
2807.	Posy vase two monkeys on coconut	3"h	40-60			
2808.	Pot		5-15			
2809.	Jug		10-25			
2810.	Bird Swan on stand		25-45			
2811.	Vase		5-20			
2812.	Bowl on foot 'Corinthus' range	14.5"l	8-12			
2813.	Monkey jug similar to 2807		40-60			

Mould No	Description	Size	Price Guide in £'s	Colour	Date Purchased	Price Paid
2814.	Bowl on foot 'Corinthus' range	7"h	8-12			
2815.	Character jug 'Robert Burns'		25-50			
2815.	Character jug 'William Shakespeare'		25-50			
2816.	Vase 'Bamboo' range	4.25"h	8-10			
2817.	Vase 'Trellis' range	6.75"l	10-20			
2818.	N/I					
2819.	Vase on foot 'Corinthus' range	10"h	5-20			
2820.	Vase		5-15			
2821.	Vase 'Trellis' range	10"h	10-20			
2822.	Figure possibly a saint	If so :-	200-250			
2823.	Bowl		5-15			
2824.	Figure St Francis of Assisi no production proto-type only	8.5"h	200-250			
2825.	Pot		5-15			
2826.	Bookend.....profile of Wagner similar to 2841	4.25"h	40-50			
2827.	Vase on foot 'Corinthus' range	8"h	15-20			
2828.	Bowl on foot 'Corinthus' range	9.5"dia	15-25			
2829.	Posy holder Boy	3.75"h	50-90			
	Girl	3.75"h	50-90			
	Other:-	3.75"h	15-25			
2830.	Plant pot holder 'Cone' range		5-15			
2831.	Vase 'Cone' range	7"h	5-20			
2832.	Low vase 'Cone' range		5-20			
2833.	Low vase 'Cone' range		5-20			

Mould No	Description	Size	Price Guide in £'s	Colour	Date Purchased	Price Paid
2834.	Vase 'Cone' range		5-20			
2835.	Bowl 'Cone' range	3.25"h 6.5"l	5-20			
2836.	Vase 'Cone' range		5-20			
2837.	N/I					
2838.	Wall pocket		20-30			
2839.	N/I					
2840.	Vase		5-20			
2841.	Vase as book with scholar's head	6"h	40-50			
2842.	Figures Pope x 2 prototypes possibly		200-250			
2843.	Long trough 'Trellis' range	13.5"l	10-15			
2844.	Vase		5-20			
2845.	Boy holding flower	3"h	60-75			
2846.	Vase 'Oakwood' range	6"h	15-20			
2847.	Vase 'Venetian' range (Twisty)		5-20			
2848.	Vase		5-20			
2849.	Pot on three feet 'Venetian' range (Twisty)		5-10			
2850-51	N/I					
2852.	Vase on three feet 'Venetian' range (Twisty)		5-1			
2853.	N/I					
2854.	Bowl 'Venetian' range (Twisty)		5-20			
2855-2856	N/I					
2857.	Plant pot 'Venetian' range (Twisty)		10-20			
2858.	N/I					

Mould No	Description	Size	Price Guide in £'s	Colour	Date Purchased	Price Paid
2859.	N/I					
2860.	Vase	8.25"h	5-20			
2861.	Vase		5-20			
2862.	Bowl as Gondola candle holder	5.25"l	20-30			
2863.	Dutch clog	4.5"l	10-20			
2864.	Vase goblet shape 'Autumn Chintz' range	7"h	10-15			
2865.	Chalice		10-15			
2866.	Book support 'Shakespeare'		25-35			
2867.	Shell vase		10-25			
2868.	Shell vase		10-25			
2869.	Shell vase		10-25			
2870.	Vase 'Apple Blossom' range	8.25"h	20-30			
2871.	Vase tall 'Apple Blossom' range		25-35			
2872.	Vase 'Apple Blossom' range	10.5"l	20-35			
2873.	Bowl		5-15			
2874.	Vase 'Apple Blossom' range	7"l	20-35			
2875.	Low vase 'Apple Blossom' range	7.75"l	12-20			
2876.	Vase 'Apple Blossom' range	6.25"h	15-30			
2877.	Plant pot holder 'Apple Blossom' range	5.75"h	20-35			
2878.	Plant pot holder 'Apple Blossom' range	4.75"h	15-25			
2879.	Vase		5-20			
2880.	Tray		5-15			
2881.	Wine cup		10-15			

Mould No	Description	Size	Price Guide in £'s	Colour	Date Purchased	Price Paid
2882.	Bowl 'Apple Blossom' range	7"l	15-25			
2883.	Bowl 'Apple Blossom' range	10.25"l	20-40			
2884.	Bowl 'Apple Blossom' range	14"l	30-40			
2885.	Plate 'Apple Blossom' range	9.25"dia	20-35			
2886.	Long posy small		8-10			
2887.	Figure 'The Virgin Mary' prototype		200-250			
2888.	Character jug 'Uncle Sam'		50-75			
2889.	Trough		8-10			
2890.	Bowl two handles		10-20			
2891.	Bowl		5-15			
2892.	Character jug 'Abraham Lincoln'		50-75			
2893.	Vase 'Bracken' range tall		15-25			
2894.	Vase 'Bracken' range	3.75"h 8.5"l	15-25			
2895.	Figure 'St Joan of Arc' prototype		200-250			
2896.	Vase	6"h	8-15			
2897.	Stocking		10-15			
2898.	N/I					
2899.	Character Jug 'John F. Kennedy'	6.25"h	30-55			
2899.	Cheese dish 'Wyka' range	6.75"w	20-30			
2900.	Vase Embossed spray		5-20			
2901.	Vase oriental style		5-15			
2902.	Vase		5-20			
2903.	Figure St Nicholas & child not produced proto-type only		200-250			

Mould No	Description	Size	Price Guide in £'s	Colour	Date Purchased	Price Paid
2904.	Vase 'Bracken' range	4.25"h	8-12			
2905.	N/I					
2906.	Plant pot 'Bracken' range	7"h	10-15			
2907.	Vase 'Jewel' range	3.75"h 6.5"l	8-12			
2908.	Bowl 'Bracken' range	3.75"h 13.75"l	10-15			
2909.	Bowl 'Bracken' range	4"h 8.75"l	10-20			
2910.	Pot		5-15			
2911.	N/I					
2912.	Giraffe lying down	5.5"h	30-45			
2913.	Tray		5-10			
2914.	Vase		5-20			
2915.	Vase		5-20			
2916.	Biscuit jar		15-20			
2917.	Wall pocket		20-30			
2918.	N/I					
2919.	Bowl	3.75"h 6.25"l	10-50			
2920.	Vase		5-20			
2921.	Plant pot 'Oakwood' range		20-30			
2922.	N/I					
2923.	Bowl 'Oaklwood' range	3.5"h	15-25			
2924.	N/I					
2925.	Vase 'Oakwood' range	11"l	15-25			
2926.	Vase 'Oakwood' range	10"h	20-30			

Mould No	Description	Size	Price Guide in £'s	Colour	Date Purchased	Price Paid
2927.	Vase 'Oaklwood' range	8"h	20-30			
2928.	Vase 'Oaklwood' range		20-30			
2929.	N/I					
2930.	Vase 'Oakwood' range		15-25			
2931.	Vase 'Oakwood' range	6.5"h 10.5"l	15-25			
2932.	Vase 'Oakwood' range	6"h 7"l	15-25			
2933.	Giraffe on all fours	6"h	50-80			
2934.	Vase		5-20			
2935.	Vase		5-20			
2936.	Vase		5-20			
2937.	Vase 'Apple Blossom' range	10"h	35-50			
2938.	Dog sad	4"h	15-25			
2939.	Wheel barrow		10-20			
2940.	Serviette ring with flowers		15-25			
2941.	Jug	6.5"h	10-15			
2942.	Vase		5-20			
2943.	N/I					
2944.	Jug	6.5"h	5-15			
2945.	Mug no handle		8-10			
2946.	Zebra		40-55			
2947.	Mug no handle		8-10			
2948.	Bowl		5-15			
2949.	Vase		5-20			

Mould No	Description	Size	Price Guide in £'s	Colour	Date Purchased	Price Paid
2950.	Dog sad	6.25"h	20-30			
2951.	Dog sad	7.25"h	25-40			
2952.	N/I					
2953.	Bowl		5-15			
2954.	Vase 'Magnolia' range	9"l	35-50			
2955.	Rabbit (original) Crouching		300-450			
2956.	Jam pot 'Wyka' range	4.5"h	10-20			
2957.	Cheese dish		15-25			
2958.	Jam pot		8-12			
2959.	Butter dish		10-15			
2960.	Tray		5-10			
2961.	Large bowl		10-20			
2962.	Dog Poodle	5.25"h	20-30			
2963.	Shell vase	2.5"h	10-15			
2964.	Shell vase		10-15			
2965.	Pot		5-10			
2966.	Teapot		30-40			
2967.	Teapot		30-40			
2968.	Small Bowl		8-10			
2969.	Teapot		20-30			
2970.	Posy factory gift	4.5"l	25-40			
2971.	Dog Poodle	4.25"h 6.5"l	25-35			
2972.	Vase		5-10			

Mould No	Description	Size	Price Guide in £'s	Colour	Date Purchased	Price Paid
2973.	Dog Dachshund lying nose to feet	5"l	25-40			
2974.	Dog pup sitting	5.5"h	25-40			
2975.	Vase		5-20			
2976.	Teapot 'Avon shape'	5.75"h	25-45			
2977.	Sugar bowl 'Avon shape'	3.25"h	5-8			
2978.	Jug small 'Avon shape'	3"h	5-10			
2979.	Vase Embossed	8"h	10-18			
2980.	Rabbit sitting up with bow tie	6"h	40-80			
2981.	Vase 'Magnolia' range	9"h	40-50			
2982.	Teapot 'Avon shape'	5"h	20-30			
2983.	Vase	9"h	10-18			
2984.	Basket		5-15			
2985.	Bowl	9.5"dia	10-20			
2986.	Watercress dish and stand	9.5"dia	15-25			
2987.	Basket		5-15			
2988.	Tray		5-15			
2989.	Bowl		5-15			
2990.	Watercress dish and stand		15-25			
2991.	Vase 'Oakwood' range	5"h 7.5"l	15-25			
2992.	Vase 'Magnolia' range	6.25"h	20-45			
2993.	Vase 'Magnolia' range	6.75"l	20-35			
2994.	N/I					
2995.	Bowl 'Magnolia' range	5"h	20-40			

Mould No	Description	Size	Price Guide in £'s	Colour	Date Purchased	Price Paid
2996.	Jug 'Wyka' range	2.75"h	10-15			
2997.	Vase 'Wyka' range	10.5"h	20-30			
2998.	Butter dish 'Wyka' range	7"l	10-15			
2999.	Cheese dish		10-20			
3000.	Bowl 'Wyka' range	11"dia	15-25			
3001.	Salt,pepper,mustard 'Wyka' range	3.75"h	20-25			
3002.	Sandwich tray 'Wyka' range	11.5"l	10-15			
3003.	Double tray 'Wyka' range	11.5"l	10-15			
3004.	Triple tray 'Wyka' range	15"l	15-20			
3005...	Toast rack 'Wyka' range	9.5"l	15-20			
3006	Vase 'Wyka' range	12.5"h	20-30			
3007	Watercress dish and stand 'Wyka' range		10-20			
3008.	N/I					
3009.	Jug 'Wyka' range	8"h	20-25			
3010.	Butter dish 'Wyka' range	7.25"l	15-18			
3011.	Vase 'Wyka' range	7.5"h	15-25			
3012.	Mug 'Wyka' range	4.5"h	5-10			
3013.	Bowl 'Wyka' range	3.5"dia	5-10			
3014.	Posy 'Oakleaf' range	9.5"l	12-15			
3015.	Vase 'Oakleaf' range	8"l	10-15			
3016.	Jug 'Bracken' range	10.25"h	20-30			
3017.	Posy		5-10			
3018.	Posy 'Bracken' range		5-10			

Mould No	Description	Size	Price Guide in £'s	Colour	Date Purchased	Price Paid
3019.	Pig money box	4.5"h 7.5"l	20-35			
3020.	Bowl 'Magnolia' range	5.5"h 7.5"dia	25-45			
3021.	N/I					
3022.	Plant pot 'Magnolia' range	5.75"h	25-45			
3023.	Vase 'Bracken' range	4"h 8.25"l	14-18			
3024.	N/I					
3025.	Vase 'Slymcraft' range	6.25"h	5-10			
3026.	Vase		5-10			
3027.	Vase		5-10			
3028.	Vase		5-10			
3029.	Vase 'Slymcraft' range	12"h	15-20			
3030.	Vase 'Slymcraft' range	7.5"h	8-12			
3031.	Vase 'Chesterfield' range	6"h	8-12			
3032.	Vase 'Slymcraft' range	8.75"h	10-15			
3033.	Vase		5-10			
3034.	Vase		5-10			
3035.	Vase		5-10			
3036.	Vase 'Slymcraft' range	7.75"h	10-15			
3037.	Vase 'Slymcraft' range	9.75"h	10-18			
3038.	Vase 'Slymcraft' range	9.5"h	10-18			
3039.	Vase 'Slymcraft' range		9-12			
3040.	Vase 'Slymcraft' range	3.75"h	5-8			

Mould No	Description	Size	Price Guide in £'s	Colour	Date Purchased	Price Paid
3041.	Vase		5-10			
3042.	Vase 'Slymcraft' range	7.75"h	10-15			
3043.	Vase 'Slymcraft' range	4.75"h	5-8			
3044.	Vase 'Slymcraft' range	7.5"h	7-12			
3045.	Vase		5-10			
3046.	Vase 'Slymcraft' range	7.5"h	8-10			
3047.	Vase 'Slymcraft' range	9.5"h	10-18			
3048.	Vase 'Slymcraft' range	7.75"h	7-10			
3049.	Vase 'Slymcraft' range	12"h	15-20			
3050.	Vase cylindrical	3"h	5-8			
3051.	Vase 'Slymcraft' range	7.5"h	8-12			
3052.	Vase 'Slymcraft' range	6.5"h	8-12			
3053.	Vase 'Chesterfield' range	10.25"h	18-22			
3054.	Vase 'Chesterfield' range	8.25"h	10-18			
3055.	Vase 'Slymcraft' range	9.5"h	10-18			
3056.	Vase 'Slymcraft' range	9.5"h	10-18			
3057.	Plant pot 'Chesterfield' range	5"h	15-20			
3058.	Plant pot 'Chesterfield' range	6"h	15-20			
3059.	Vase 'Slymcraft' range	7.75"h	8-12			
3060.	Vase		8-12			
3061.	Vase 'Slymcraft' range	9.75"h	10-18			
3062.	Vase 'Slymcraft' range	7.5"h	8-12			
3063.	Vase 'Slymcraft' range	5.5"h	5-8			

Mould No	Description	Size	Price Guide in £'s	Colour	Date Purchased	Price Paid
3064.	Vase specimen 'Slymcraft' range	10"h	10-15			
3065.	Vase 'Slymcraft' range	3.5"h	5-8			
3066.	Vase 'Slymcraft' range	5.5"h	5-8			
3067.	Vase 'Slymcraft' range	10"h	10-15			
3068.	Bowl 'Slymcraft' range	5.5"dia	5-8			
3069.	Vase 'Chesterfield' range	9.5"l	5-10			
3070.	Vase		5-10			
3071.	Bowl 'Slymcraft' range	7.75"dia	8-12			
3072.	Vase long	6.5"l	4-8			
3073.	Vase		5-10			
3074.	Dog		80-100			
3075.	Cat Manx	3.5"h	45-75			
3076.	Flower holder		10-15			
3077.	Dog Dachshund	6.5"h	50-75			
3078.	Dog Dachshund	5"h	30-45			
3079.	N/I					
3080.	Basket		10-15			
3081.	Bowl		10-15			
3082.	Vase		5-10			
3083.	Bowl		10-15			
3084.	Vase long low		10-15			
3085.	Dish banana shape 'Slymcraft'	10"l	4-10			
3086.	Ashtray round used for advertising	6.25"dia	10-20			

Mould No	Description	Size	Price Guide in £'s	Colour	Date Purchased	Price Paid
3087.	N/I					
3088.	Zebra		45-65			
3089.	Vase		5-12			
3090.	N/I					
3091.	N/I					
3092.	Dog Spaniel	4"h	20-35			
3093.	Toothache dog	4"h	35-50			
3094.	N/I					
3095.	N/I					
3096.	Dog Terrier	4.5"h	30-60			
3097.	Rabbit	5.5"h	50-75			
3098.	Vase 'Lily' range	6.5"l	30-45			
3099.	Candle holder		8-12			
3100.	Flower trough 'Chesterfield' range0	7.5"l	15-2			
3101.	Posy vase 'Lily ' range	10"l	50-70			
3102.	Kitten chasing tail		150-200			
3103.	N/I					
3104.	Vase		5-12			
3105.	Ashtray		2-5			
3106.	Character jug 'Robert Burns'	5.75"h	35-55			
3107.	Vase		5-12			
3108.	Bowl 'Bracken' range	5"h	10-15			
3109.	N/I					

Mould No	Description	Size	Price Guide in £'s	Colour	Date Purchased	Price Paid
3110.	Dog Poodle	4.75"h	25-35			
3111.	Wall vase		20-30			
3111.	Girl 'Pam'	3"h	65-105			
3112.	Boy 'Paul'	2.75"h	65-105			
3113.	Boy 'Pete'	3.25"h	65-105			
3114.	Dog puppy	3"h	20-35			
3115.	Duckling	1.5"h	40-55			
3116.	Dog puppy	2.25"h	20-35			
3117.	Duckling	2"h	50-75			
3118.	Dog puppy	3.5"h	30-50			
3119.	Horse	5.5"h	25-35			
3120.	Hare	4"h	75-95			
3121.	Cat scared	2.5"h	45-60			
3122.	Ashtray		20-30			
3122.	Ash tray with dog or wall clock		35-50			
3123.	Mongrel sitting	5.5"h	70-90			
3124.	Dog Dachshund	4.5"h	25-45			
3125.	Dog small Bulldog		40-70			
3126.	Dog lying down	4"h	40-80			
3127.	Rabbit		50-60			
3128.	Dog Corgi sitting	4.25"h	15-55			
3129.	Horse with riding gear	5.5"h	30-45			
3130.	Horse standing	5.5"h	30-40			

Mould No	Description	Size	Price Guide in £'s	Colour	Date Purchased	Price Paid
3131.	Donkey kicking out		35-75			
3132.	Dog with with baskets	2.25"h	50-80			
3133.	Puppy Corgi sitting	2.5"h	18-35			
3134.	Puppy Corgi very small	1.5"h	18-35			
3135.	Puppy Corgi lying down	2"h	18-35			
3136.	Dog Corgi on all fours	4"h	25-40			
3137.	Puppy Corgi on all fours	2.75"h	18-35			
3138.	Donkey and cart or panniers	4"h	30-50			
3139.	Donkey	4"h	25-35			
3140.	Elephant caricature with big ears	5"l	80-120			
3141.	Monkey with boxing gloves	4.75"h	50-90			
3142.	Dog		35-75			
3143.	Dog Spaniel pup	3"h	30-75			
3144.	Horse with head down	5"h	25-40			
3145.	Foal standing	4.25"h	25-40			
3146.	Cockerel		65-100			
3147.	Donkey with amused expression		55-95			
3148.	N/I					
3149.	Cart horse		35-50			
3150.	Foal on all fours	4"h	20-30			
3151.	Cat lying down	5.5"h	60-90			
3152.	Horse standing	10"h	60-90			
3152.	Zebra	10"h	70-95			

Mould No	Description	Size	Price Guide in £'s	Colour	Date Purchased	Price Paid
3153.	Tiger lying down	5.5"h 7.5"l	60-90			
3154.	Stag lying down	6.5"h 7.25"l	60-90			
3155.	Cart horse	6.5"h	45-65			
3156.	Swallow wall plaque	6.5"l	40-65			
3157.	Swallow wall plaque	5"l	25-50			
3158.	Swallow wall plaque	4.5"l	20-40			
3159.	N/I					
3160.	N/I					
3161.	N/I					
3162.	Grebe on foot to go in bowl	3.5"h	35-60			
3163.	Cat sitting	2"h	25-45			
3164.	Dog Pekinese puppy	2.5"h	25-35			
3165.	Dog Pekinese	3"h	30-40			
3166.	Dog Stafford Bull Terrier	4.5"h	40-50			
3167.	Cat sitting	5"h	50-85			
3168.	Kitten in ball of wool	2.75"h	20-35			
3169.	Dog Golden Retriever	5"h	25-35			
3170.	Dog Alsation	5.75"h	20-40			
3171.	Dog Alsation	4"h	30-40			
3172.	Goat	5"h	50-90			
3173.	Dog Chow on all fours	4.75"h	20-35			
3174.	Dog Poodle frolicking	5.75"h	25-45			
3175.	Dog Dachshund on hind legs	5.5"h	60-85			

Mould No	Description	Size	Price Guide in £'s	Colour	Date Purchased	Price Paid
3176.	Horse standing	7.25"h	25-35			
3177.	Dog Sealyham puppy	5"h	50-90			
3178.	Dog Sealyham		30-60			
3179.	Dog Sealyham	4"h	45-65			
3180.	Horse	9"h	35-50			
3180.	Horse and trap	17.5"l	55-85			
3181.	Cat Money box		35-75			
3182.	Dog cartoon style Goofy	5.5"h	60-85			
3183.	'Toothache dog'	5.25"h	50-70			
3184.	N/I					
3185.	Bowl		8-10			
3186.	Tray		8-12			
3187.	Dog condiment set salt pepper mustard		85-120			
3188.	Bowl 'Chesterfield' range		10-15			
3189.	Vase 'Slymcraft' long low	14.5"l	10-15			
3190.	Bowl 'Chesterfield' range	9.25"l	10-20			
3191.	Bowl		10-15			
3192.	Vase		10-20			
3193.	Bulb bowl brick pattern	9"l	12-20			
3194.	Bulb bowl brick pattern	6.25"l	12-18			
3195.	Bowl		10-15			
3196.	Bowl 'Magnolia' range	8"dia	45-75			
3197.	Basket		10-15			

Mould No	Description	Size	Price Guide in £'s	Colour	Date Purchased	Price Paid
3198-3202	N/I					
3203.	Jug	5.75"h	10-20			
3204.	Jug small 'Avon' shape	3.5"h	8-10			
3205.	N/I					
3206.	Butter dish 'Avon' shape	7"l	15-20			
3207.	Cheese dish 'Avon' shape		15-20			
3208.	Sandwich Tray 'Avon' shape	12.5"l	10-15			
3209.	Honey jar 'Avon' shape	4"h	5-10			
3210.	Vase low trellis design	7.5"l	10-15			
3211.	Vase	9"l	10-15			
3212.	Bowl	6"l	10-15			
3213.	Bowl 'Magnolia' long oval	13.5"l	25-40			
3214.	Bowl 'Magnolia' range oval0	4.25"l	20-3			
3215.	Trough 'Magnolia' range	7.5"l	15-25			
3216.	Vase 'Magnolia' range	10"h	55-70			
3217.	Vase 'Magnolia' range	8"h	30-50			
3218.	Bowl 'Magnolia' range round	6.5"dia	15-30			
3219.	Tankard	5"h	15-20			
3220.	Tankard	5"h	15-20			
3221.	Vase 'Magnolia' range 2 handled	12"l	45-60			
3222.	Bowl		8-12			
3223.	Log vase		8-12			
3224.	Bowl		8-12			

Mould No	Description	Size	Price Guide in £'s	Colour	Date Purchased	Price Paid
3225.	Vase 'Slymcraft' range 2 handled	14"l	15-25			
3226.	Tankard embossed wild ducks	5"h	15-20			
3227.	Bowl		10-15			
3228.	Vase		10-15			
3229.	N/I					
3230.	Vase fish shape	7"h	15-20			
3231.	Triple candle holder	13"l	20-28			
3232.	Vase		10-15			
3233.	Bowl log shape	8"l	15-20			
3234.	Bowl log shape	4.5"l	10-15			
3235.	Bowl log shape	4"l	8-12			
3236.	Vase		10-15			
3237.	Tray		8-12			
3238.	Cup 'Avon' shape	3"h	5-8			
3239.	Elephant money box	4.25"h	50-90			
3239.	Elephant with posy on back	4.5"h	30-45			
3240.	Pig		25-30			
3241.	Posy holder scottie dog		25-40			
3242.	N/I					
3243.	Bowl	8.75"l	15-20			
3244.	Bowl	6"l	15-20			
3245.	Jar		15-20			
3246.	Bowl		15-20			

Mould No	Description	Size	Price Guide in £'s	Colour	Date Purchased	Price Paid
3247.	Vase 'Lily' range	10"h	40-60			
3248.	N/I					
3249.	Bowl		10-15			
3250.	Vase		10-15			
3251.	Bowl		10-15			
3252.	Vase		10-15			
3253.	Cup		2-5			
3254.	Bowl		10-15			
3255.	Vase 'Chesterfield' range	10"h	15-25			
3256.	Vase 'Chesterfield' range	8"h	15-25			
3257.	Plate 2 scroll handle	9"dia	10-12			
3258.	Jug small		8-10			
3259.	Bowl		8-10			
3260.	Bowl		10-15			
3261.	Vase 'Fuchsia' range		20-30			
3261.	Plate	10"dia	8-10			
3262.	Bowl 'Fuchsia' boat shape also	14"l	30-40			
3262.	Plate	8"dia	12-18			
3262.	Bowl 'Fuchsia' range	3.5"h 14"l	25-35			
3263.	Vase 'Fuchsia' range		20-25			
3263.	Plate	6.5"dia	10-14			
3264.	Bowl	6.25"dia	10-16			
3264.	Jardiniere 'Fuchsia' range	9"l	30-40			

Mould No	Description	Size	Price Guide in £'s	Colour	Date Purchased	Price Paid
3265.	Trough 'Fuchsia' range	7.75"l	15-20			
3265.	Fruit bowl 'Avon' shape		10-15			
3266.	Vase 'Fuchsia' range	6.75"l	15-20			
3266.	Cake plate 'Avon' shape	10.5"dia	8-10			
3267.	Cake stand single tier 'Avon' shape	8"dia	15-20			
3267.	Jardiniere 'Fuchsia' range	6"h	20-30			
3268.	Cake stand 2 tier 'Avon' shape		20-25			
3268.	Vase 'Fuchsia' range	9"h	25-30			
3269.	Vase 'Fuchsia' range	7.75"h	20-25			
3269.	Fruit bowl 'Avon' shape	8.5"dia	12-18			
3270.	Plant pot 'Fuchsia' range	5"h	15-20			
3270.	Soup bowl 'Avon' shape		12-18			
3271.	Plant pot 'Fuchsia' range		15-20			
3272.	Vase 'Fuchsia' range	12"l	20-25			
3273.	Tankard embossed fox mask	3.75"h	12-20			
3274.	Tankard embossed hound head	3.75"h	12-20			
3274.	Tankard also 1972 Stoke City cup final	3.75"h	20-40			
3275.	Dog Spaniel with pipe	5.25"h	40-70			
3276.	Dog Spaniel with ball	3.25"h	40-70			
3277.	Vase		10-15			
3278.	Tankard embossed horse head	3.75"h	12-20			
3279.	Character jug George Bernard Shaw	5.5"h	35-60			
3280.	Bowl log shape	6"l	8-12			

Mould No	Description	Size	Price Guide in £'s	Colour	Date Purchased	Price Paid
3281.	Cup		3-5			
3282.	Flower jug	15"h	30-50			
3283.	Vase 'Lily' range	8.25"h	35-45			
3284.	Vase		5-10			
3285.	Vase 'Lily' range large	10"l	45-55			
3286.	Vase 'Lily' range	12"h	55-70			
3287.	Bowl 'Lily' range oval	9.5"l	30-45			
3288.	Plant pot 'Lily' range	8"dia	45-55			
3289.	Posy 'Lily' range	7.25"l	25-35			
3290.	Vase 'Lily' range	11.5"h	50-65			
3291.	Plant pot 'Lily' range	7"dia	30-45			
3292.	Bowl 'Lily' range		25-35			
3293-3295	N/I					
3296.	Condiment set 'Avon' shape 4 piece		15-20			
3297.	Cheese board + knife 'Avon' shape	9.75"l	15-20			
3298.	Vase		5-10			
3299.	Toast rack 'Avon' shape	7.5"l	15-20			
3300.	N/I					
3301.	N/I					
3302.	Vase		10-15			
3303.	Vase		10-15			
3304.	Beaker		8-12			
3305.	Vase		10-15			

Mould No	Description	Size	Price Guide in £'s	Colour	Date Purchased	Price Paid
3306.	Tankard		10-15			
3307.	Cat factory prototype	13"h	100-150			
3308.	Vase		10-15			
3309.	Vase		10-15			
3310.	Vase 'Slymcraft' oval		10-15			
3311.	Bowl with bird		45-55			
3312.	Vase	6.5"h	10-18			
3313.	Cupid flower holder	3.75"h	15-20			
3314.	Dog Fox Terrier	5.75"h	30-50			
3315.	Coffee pot 'Avon' shape 2 pint	9"h	10-20			
3316.	Vase	8.5"h	10-20			
3317.	Dog standing Wire Haired Fox Terrier	5.5"h	30-50			
3318.	Dog lying asleep Wire Haired Fox Terrier	5"l	30-50			
3319.	Puppy dog sitting		25-38			
3320.	Puppy dog Dachshund sitting	4.5"l	25-40			
3321.	Dog Alsatian sitting	6"h	25-40			
3322.	Lop eared rabbit medium	8.25"h	90-130			
3323.	Vase	6.25"h	12-18			
3324.	Vase	10"h	18-20			
3325.	Cupid flower holder round	4.5"h	12-18			
3326.	Lop eared rabbit large	12.5"h	250-300			
3327.	Rabbit ears up	12"h	250-300			
3328.	Rabbit ears up	8"h	100-140			

Mould No	Description	Size	Price Guide in £'s	Colour	Date Purchased	Price Paid
3329.	Vase Shell range	7"h	15-20			
3330.	Vase	8"h	12-18			
3331.	Plant pot ribbed		12-18			
3332.	Plant pot square		12-18			
3333.	Cupid flower holder	4.5"h	12-18			
3334.	Vase sea shell	5"l	12-18			
3335.	Dog Spaniel sitting		30-50			
3336.	Flower pot square ribbed		8-12			
3337.	Pig	3.5"l 2"h	25-35			
3338.	Dog sitting Highland Terrier		25-40			
3339.	Bird Osprey 'Prestige piece'	8.5"h	60-100			
3340.	Ginger jar and cover	6"h	10-20			
3341.	Vase 'Opelle' range oval		10-15			
3342.	Vase	7"h	10-18			
3343.	Vase	5.5"h	8-12			
3344.	Vase	5"h	8-12			
3345.	Vase long low		8-12			
3346.	Pig's head money box		60-90			
3347.	Vase fluted	7.5"h	15-20			
3348.	Vase	10.5"l	15-20			
3349.	Vase 'Pebbles' range	10"l	18-25			
3350.	Vase 'Pebbles' range	6.75"h	12-18			
3351.	Plant pot 'Alpine' range		15-20			

Mould No	Description	Size	Price Guide in £'s	Colour	Date Purchased	Price Paid
3352.	Ginger jar embossed		10-15			
3353.	Coffee pot 'Avon' small		18-25			
3354.	Covered jar square		8-12			
3355.	Bowl 'Pebbles' range	6.75"dia	15-20			
3356.	Bowl oblong with figure		25-30			
3357.	Jar 'Blossom' range		8-12			
3358.	Vase 'Pebbles' range	9"h	15-25			
3359.	Jar square etched		8-12			
3360.	Posy vase 'Pebble' range	11.5"l	15-20			
3361.	Plant pot 'Pebble' range	4.5"h	10-18			
3362.	Vase flat sides	5"h	8-12			
3363.	Posy vase	8.5"l	5-10			
3364.	Vase 'Alpine' range	8"h	10-20			
3365.	Posy vase	6.5"l	5-10			
3366.	Posy vase	4"l	4-8			
3367.	Square jar etched pattern		20-30			
3368.	Vase 'Pebbles' range	11.25"h	18-25			
3369.	Vase rope handles 'Alpine' range	8"h	10-20			
3370.	Sea Horse with shell bowl	10"h	25-35			
3371.	Vase rope handles 'Alpine' range	11"h	15-25			
3372.	Tea caddy elephant head handles 'Rington's'	7.5"h	20-25			
3373.	Vase	3.25"h	5-8			
3374.	Vase etched pattern	5.5"h	8-12			

Mould No	Description	Size	Price Guide in £'s	Colour	Date Purchased	Price Paid
3375.	Vase embossed pattern	5.5"h	8-12			
3376.	Vase	5.5"h	5-8			
3377.	Plant pot	5"h	12-18			
3378.	Tray 'Feather' range	7.5"l	10-15			
3379.	Vase rope handles 'Alpine' range	8"h	10-20			
3380.	Vase rope handle 'Alpine' range	8"h	10-20			
3381.	Vase 'Alpine' range	11"l	18-22			
3382.	Vase 'Alpine' range	6"h	5-10			
3383.	Mule comical sitting	6.5"h	50-90			
3384.	Mule comical standing	6.5"h	50-90			
3385.	Vase rope sides 'Alpine' range	8"h	10-20			
3386.	Vase rope sides 'Alpine' range		10-20			
3387.	Bowl rope sides 'Alpine' range	Small	10-15			
3388.	Bowl rope sides 'Alpine' range	Large	12-20			
3389.	Pot rope sides 'Alpine' range		15-25			
3390.	Pot rope sides 'Alpine' range		12-18			
3391.	Posy bar rope sides 'Alpine' range		5-10			
3392.	Cat long neck embossed with flowers	12.75"h	70-100			
3393.	Duck	4.5"h	45-60			
3394.	Ashtray for pipe textured	4.75"l	12-18			
3395.	Pot small 'Alpine' range for ferns		12-18			
3396.	Pot large 'Alpine' range for ferns		15-25			
3397.	Flower Jug 'Alpine' range	10"h	20-30			

Mould No	Description	Size	Price Guide in £'s	Colour	Date Purchased	Price Paid
3398.	Vase 'Alpine' range	9"h	12-20			
3399.	Vase 'Alpine' range	8"h	10-18			
3400.	Vase 'Alpine' range	6"h	5-10			
3401.	Bowl large 'Alpine' range oval		10-20			
3403.	Cat Long neck	7"h	35-45			
3404.	Cat Siamese caricature	6.5"h	25-45			
3405.	Jar	6"h	5-10			
3406.	Cat caricature back paw scratching	4.75"h	50-70			
3407.	Cat caricature front paw in ear.	4.5"h	50-70			
3408.	Beaker		5-10			
3409.	Ashtray pipe	4.75"l	5-10			
3410.	Ashtray as box		5-12			
3411.	Mug		8-12			
3412.	Vase		5-10			
3413.	Beaker ears of wheat		8-12			
3414.	Sea Horse vase	8"h	25-35			
3415.	Plant pot 'Pebbles' range	6"h	20-25			
3416.	Vase		5-10			
3417.	Covered jar		8-12			
3418.	Puppy dog Shetland Sheepdog		40-75			
3419.	Bowl 'Pebbles' range	6.5"l	8-12			
3420.	Posy vase 'Pebbles' range	7.5"l	8-12			
3421.	Honey pot		8-12			

Mould No	Description	Size	Price Guide in £'s	Colour	Date Purchased	Price Paid
3422.	Dog Spaniel 'Big Ead' range	3.75"h	40-70			
3423.	Dog English sheepdog 'Big Ead' range	3"h	40-70			
3424.	Dog Pekinese 'Big Ead' range	2.75"h	30-65			
3425.	Dog Alsatian 'Big Ead' range	3.5"h	30-65			
3426.	Dog Dachshund 'Big Ead' range	3"h	30-65			
3427.	Dog St Bernard 'Big Ead' range	3"h	30-65			
3428.	Dog Poodle 'Funnies' range	3.5"h	30-65			
3429.	Dog Bulldog 'Big Ead' range	3"h	30-65			
3430.	Dog Shetland Sheepdog 'Funnies' range	3.5"h	30-65			
3431.	Dog Scottie 'Big Ead' range	3.25"h	30-65			
3432.	Dog Yorkshire Terrier 'Big Ead' range	3"h	40-60			
3433.	Dog with mouth open 'Big Ead' range	4.25"h	60-70			
3434.	Vase long low 'Pebbles' range	13.5"l	15-20			
3435.	Ash box horses		15-20			
3436.	Ashbox fish		15-20			
3437.	Ashbox duck		15-20			
3438.	Plinth		2-3			
3439.	Bowl 'Pebbles' range	9.75"l	10-18			
3440.	Bowl 'Pebbles' range	6.5"l	8-15			
3441.	Vase	6"h	5-12			
3442.	Beaker		5-8			
3443.	Vase oval 'Chequers' range	8"h	10-20			
3444.	Vase 'Chequers' range		8-15			

Mould No	Description	Size	Price Guide in £'s	Colour	Date Purchased	Price Paid
3445.	Sea horse with shell bowl small		20-30			
3446.	Basket		8-12			
3447.	Dog Cairn Terrier	5"h	20-35			
3448.	Vase		5-10			
3449.	Vase 'Opelle' range	6"h	5-10			
3450.	Vase 'Opelle' range	8"h	10-20			
3451.	Vase 'Opelle' range	10"h	18-22			
3452.	Tea cup embossed		6-10			
3453.	Posy 'Opelle' range		5-10			
3454.	Hors d'oeuvre tray with six dishes		20-25			
3455.	Plant pot 'Opelle' range large		15-25			
3456.	Plant pot 'Opelle' range small		10-15			
3457.	Cat Siamese caricature	13"h	50-80			
3458.	Vase 'Opelle' range		5-10			
3459.	Otter with fish 'Prestige' range	9.5"l	150-220			
3460.	Vase 'Sea Horse' range	10"h	30-40			
3461.	Bowl oblong 'Opelle' range large	5"h	10-25			
3462.	Bowl oblong 'Opelle' range small		8-18			
3463.	Bowl square		10-15			
3464.	Planter	15"l	5-10			
3465.	Flower bowl 'Opelle' range	9.5"sq	10-20			
3466.	Wall vase 'Opelle' range		15-22			
3467.	Ashtray		2-5			

Mould No	Description	Size	Price Guide in £'s	Colour	Date Purchased	Price Paid
3468.	Cup fluted		3-5			
3469.	N/I					
3470.	Posy 'Sea Horse' range	8"l	12-18			
3471.	Posy 'Sea Horse' range	8.5"l	12-18			
3472.	Vase 'Sea Horse' range	6"h	10-15			
3473.	Vase 'Sea Horse' range small		18-22			
3474.	Bowl 'Sea Horse' range large		18-22			
3475.	Bowl 'Sea Horse' range small	5"h	15-2			
3476.	Plant pot 'Sea Horse' range		20-25			
3477.	Vase 'Tudor' range small		5-8			
3478.	Shaving mug	4.25"h	10-15			
3479.	Bowl		8-12			
3480.	Plant pot 'Pebbles' range	5.25"h	15-20			
3481.	Ashtray/dish 'Pebbles' range	5.5"l	5-10			
3482.	Dish 'Pebbles' range on feet	12.5"l	15-25			
3483.	Vase	5"h	8-12			
3484.	Celery tray 'Feather' range	13.5"l	20-25			
3485.	Salad bowl 'Feather' range	12"dia	20-25			
3486.	Desert bowl	3.5"h	5-8			
3487.	Vase panel front	10"h	18-22			
3488.	Tankard plain	3.75"h	8-10			
3488.	Tankard Nottingham Forest FC	3.75"h	20-40			
3489.	Powder bowl and cover shaped		10-15			

Mould No	Description	Size	Price Guide in £'s	Colour	Date Purchased	Price Paid
3490.	Vase 'Tudor' range	6"h	8-12			
3491.	Vase 'Tudor' range	8"h	10-20			
3492.	Vase 'Tudor' range	10"h	18-22			
3493.	Vase 'Tudor' range large		18-22			
3494.	Vase 'Tudor' range small		5-8			
3495.	Bowl 'Tudor' range		8-12			
3496.	Pot 'Tudor' range large		12-20			
3497.	Pot 'Tudor' range small		10-15			
3498.	Vase posy 'Tudor' range large		5-10			
3499.	Vase posy 'Tudor' range small		5-8			
3500.	Dog Labrador	5"h	25-35			
3501.	Vase	9"h	12-20			
3502.	Twin tray 'Feather' range	10"l	20-25			
3503.	Triple tray 'Feather' range	12"l	20-25			
3504.	Dish 'Feather' range	12"l	20-25			
3505.	Condiment set & tray 'Feather'range	8.75"l	25-30			
3506.	Twin tray 'Feather' range	11"l	20-25			
3507.	Cress dish & stand 'Feather' range	10"dia	20-25			
3508.	Cheese dish 'Feather' range		25-30			
3509.	Biscuit jar 'Feather' range		20-25			
3510.	Quadruple tray 'Feather' range	14.5"l	25-30			
3511.	Lidded butter dish 'Feather' range	6.5"l	25-30			
3512.	Double dish 'Feather' range	11"l	25-30			

Mould No	Description	Size	Price Guide in £'s	Colour	Date Purchased	Price Paid
3513.	Beaker 'Feather' range		15-20			
3514.	Jam/honey pot 'Feather' range		15-20			
3515.	Dish 'Feather' range	5.5"l	10-15			
3516.	Tea cup		3-5			
3517.	Vase panel front large		12-20			
3518.	Vase panel front small		5-10			
3519.	Cup		3-5			
3520.	Butter dish		12-18			
3521.	Vase posy		5-8			
3522.	Dog Spaniel	5.25"h	40-65			
3523.	Vase 'New Shell' range	8"h	10-18			
3524.	Vase conch 'New Shell' range	10"h	25-30			
3525.	Vase wide 'New Shell' range large		10-20			
3526.	Vase 'New Shell' range	5.75"h	10-15			
3527.	Wall vase 'New Shell' range		20-30			
3528.	Posy 'New Shell' range	11"l	10-15			
3529.	Vase 'New Shell' range	7.5"l	12-18			
3530.	Bow 'New Shell' range small		8-12			
3531.	Bowl 'New Shell' range large		20-25			
3532.	Posy 'New Shell' range	7.5"l	8-10			
3533.	Bowl on foot small		5-10			
3534.	Bowl on foot large		10-15			
3535.	Vase		5-10			

Mould No	Description	Size	Price Guide in £'s	Colour	Date Purchased	Price Paid
3536.	Posy vase		5-10			
3537.	Bowl fluted		8-12			
3538.	Vase	6"h	8-12			
3539.	Vase 'Tudor' range	6"h	8-12			
3540.	Vase 'Slymcraft' range	8"h	10-20			
3541.	Vase 'Tudor' range	8"h	10-20			
3542.	Mr SylvaC Advertising model	8"h	150-200			
3542.	Modern version of Mr SylvaC	8"h	40-60			
3543.	Cup		3-5			
3544.	Cup		3-5			
3545.	Bowl	2"h	5-8			
3546.	Beer mug Le Moulin de Lecq Inn ?	3.5"h	15-20			
3547.	Cup and saucer 'Magnolia' range		10-25			
3548.	Vase on foot	8"h	12-18			
3549.	Vase on foot	8.25"h	12-18			
3550.	Lamp base	15.5"h	30-35			
3551.	Vase		5-10			
3552.	Dog Pug	4.5"h	25-40			
3553.	Urn 'Vintage' range	7"h	12-18			
3554.	Butter dish butterfly handle		20-25			
3555.	Bowl	4"dia	8-12			
3556.	Posy log vase		5-8			
3556.	Posy log vase with animal		25-30			

Mould No	Description	Size	Price Guide in £'s	Colour	Date Purchased	Price Paid
3557.	Vase 'Lily' range	8"h	30-40			
3558.	Vase	13"h	15-25			
3559.	Urn 'Vintage' range	5"h	10-15			
3560.	Vase dog jumping wall	3.25"h	30-35			
3560.	Mug for dentures With protruding teeth		35-45			
3561.	Dog Basset Hound sitting	6.75"h	25-40			
3561.	Cockerel ? prototype Large size		100-200			
3562.	Bowl 'New Shell' range	12"dia	10-20			
3562.	Cockerel ? prototype		100-200			
3563.	Dog Basset Hound sitting	5.75"h	25-40			
3564.	Tea cup butterfly on handle	3"h	15-20			
3565.	Dog Scottie small	2.5"h	25-40			
3566.	Barrel box		10-15			
3567.	Dog Spaniel small	2.5"h	25-40			
3568.	Giraffe	10"h	100-150			
3569.	Jug 'Avon' shape 1 pint	5.5"h	10-20			
3570.	Elephant sitting		100-150			
3571.	Basket and kitten		35-55			
3572.	Vase two handles		8-12			
3573.	Bowl	5"dia	8-12			
3574.	Not used (figure cricketers)					
3575.	Hare 'cockle shells'	7"h	50-95			
3576.	Honey pot with butterfly	4.5"h	15-20			

Mould No	Description	Size	Price Guide in £'s	Colour	Date Purchased	Price Paid
3577.	Vase		5-10			
3578.	Urn 'Vintage' range	9.5"h	15-20			
3579.	Urn 'Vintage' range	11"h	15-25			
3580.	Frog 'Cockleshells'	4"h	50-95			
3581.	Vegetable dish		12-20			
3582.	Soup bowl		5-8			
3583.	Penguin 'Cockleshells'	5.25"h	50-95			
3584.	Flower Jug on foot	11"h	20-30			
3585.	Bird Toucan 'Cockleshells'	4.5"h	50-95			
3586.	Dog lying down 'Cockleshells'	3"h	50-9			
3587.	Vase on feet	8"h	12-18			
3588.	Bowl fluted	11"dia	12-18			
3589.	Cheese board with dish		12-20			
3590.	Pot woven pattern	4"h	10-15			
3591.	Vase on feet	6"h	8-12			
3592.	Bowl on foot	11"dia	12-22			
3593.	Vase	6"h	10-20			
3594.	Meat dish oval	15.5"l	15-25			
3595.	Vase	8"h	10-20			
3596.	Jug 'Feather' range		18-25			
3597.	Pot woven pattern		10-15			
3598.	Vase oval		5-10			
3599.	Sugar bowl 'Feather' range		10-15			

Mould No	Description	Size	Price Guide in £'s	Colour	Date Purchased	Price Paid
3600.	Jug 'Feather' range small		15-25			
3601.	Jug 'Feather' range large	6.5"h	20-30			
3602.	Vase embossed		5-10			
3603.	Vase embossed	8.5"h	10-15			
3604.	Jug butterfly handle		10-20			
3605.	Pot		5-8			
3606.	Cream jug butterfly handle		15-20			
3607.	Sugar bowl butterfly handle		15-20			
3608.	Bowl fluted	6"dia	8-12			
3609.	Coffee can		3-5			
3610.	Cat 'Cockle shells' range	4.75"h	50-95			
3611.	Gravy boat and stand		12-18			
3612.	Mouse 'Cockle shells' range	3.75"h	50-95			
3613.	Honey pot bee hive	4.5"h	45-75			
3614.	Dog sitting bow round neck	5"h	40-55			
3615.	Dog	5"h	40-55			
3616.	Pot embossed		10-15			
3617.	Baby mug two handled #	3.5"h	20-30			
3618.	Vase	11"l	18-22			
3619.	Condiment set on stand butterfly		25-30			
3620.	Tea pot butterfly handle		20-35			
3621.	Ashtray	6"l	2-5			
3622.	Jar three cornered		5-10			

Mould No	Description	Size	Price Guide in £'s	Colour	Date Purchased	Price Paid
3623.	Pot embossed		5-10			
3624.	Bowl 'Privet' range	7"dia	8-15			
3625.	Bowl stone wall effect		8-12			
3626.	Top hat	4"h	10-15			
3627.	Jar		5-10			
3628.	Coffee pot		15-25			
3629.	Jar three cornered		5-10			
3630.	Coffee pot		15-25			
3631.	Vase		5-10			
3632.	Beer tankard	5"h	10-12			
3633.	Meat dish	12"l	12-20			
3634.	Mug		8-12			
3635.	Sugar bowl		5-10			
3636.	Tray	14.5"l	8-12			
3637.	Jar embossed	6"h	5-10			
3638.	Bowl stone wall effect	9.5"dia	10-20			
3639.	Vase two handles	12.5"h	15-25			
3640.	Coffee pot embossed		15-25			
3641.	Ashtray		3-6			
3642.	Dog Basset hound		25-45			
3643.	Vase stone wall effect	9"h	12-20			
3644.	Bowl large		15-25			
3645.	Tray		8-12			

Mould No	Description	Size	Price Guide in £'s	Colour	Date Purchased	Price Paid
3646.	Mug embossed		8-12			
3647.	Coffee pot 'Web' pattern		15-25			
3648.	Sugar bowl small		5-8			
3649.	Sugar bowl large		5-10			
3650.	Mug 'Web' pattern		8-12			
3651.	Vase	13"h	15-25			
3652.	Vase small		8-12			
3653.	Vase stone wall effect		10-15			
3654.	Vase	11"h	18-22			
3655.	Vase on foot	10"h	18-22			
3656.	Vase	8"h	12-20			
3657.	Vase	6"h	5-12			
3658.	Pot small		10-15			
3659.	Pot large		15-20			
3660.	Ashtray on three feet		8-10			
3661.	Beer mug one pint	5.5"h	12-18			
3662.	Vase	6"h	5-10			
3663.	Bowl on foot small		8-12			
3664.	Mug on foot		8-12			
3665.	Bowl on foot medium		10-15			
3666.	Bowl on foot large		10-20			
3667.	Sugar bowl on foot	2.5"h	5-8			
3668.	Tea pot on foot		20-30			

Mould No	Description	Size	Price Guide in £'s	Colour	Date Purchased	Price Paid
3669.	Cream jug on foot	3.5"h	5-8			
3670.	Coffee pot		15-25			
3671.	Tea cup on foot		3-5			
3672.	Tea cup embossed on foot		3-5			
3673.	Butter dish round on foot		15-20			
3674.	Ashtray tyre	5.5"dia	5-10			
3675.	Grandfather clock	2"h	25-35			
3676.	Jar	6"h	5-10			
3677.	Cheese dish square on foot		15-20			
3678.	Vase 'Palm Leaf' range	8"h	12-18			
3679.	Butter dish oblong butterfly handle		20-25			
3680.	Pot 'New shell' range		12-18			
3681.	Bowl fluted		10-15			
3682.	Ashtray	4"l	3-8			
3683.	Lamp base 'Pebble' range	12"h	30-40			
3684.	Posy vase shell shape	6.5"h	10-15			
3685.	Honey pot on foot	4.5"h	8-10			
3686.	Butter dish oblong on foot		12-18			
3687.	Coffee pot on foot large		20-30			
3688.	Beaker		8-10			
3689.	Vase		5-10			
3690.	Vase 'Palm Leaf' range	8"h	12-18			
3691.	Covered bowl	4"h	8-12			

Mould No	Description	Size	Price Guide in £'s	Colour	Date Purchased	Price Paid
3692.	Vase 'Chequers' range large		18-22			
3693.	Vase 'Chequers' range medium		10-15			
3694.	Vase 'Chequers' range	8"h	10-15			
3695.	Vase 'Chequers' range small		8-12			
3696.	Bowl on foot 'New shell' range	5.75"l	8-12			
3697.	Bowl	10"dia	10-20			
3698.	Bowl 'Chequers' range	6.75"l	10-15			
3699.	Plant pot 'Chequers' range large		15-25			
3700.	Plant pot 'Chequers' range medium		15-25			
3701.	Plant pot 'Chequers' range small		12-18			
3702.	Posy bar		5-10			
3703.	Posy 'Chequers' range		5-10			
3704.	Vase 'Chequers' range	4.5"h	5-8			
3705.	Vase 'Chequers' range	6.5"h	8-12			
3706.	Menu holder	6"h	15-20			
3707.	Posy on foot		5-10			
3708.	Butter dish		12-20			
3709.	Card holder	3"l	10-15			
3710.	Bowl 'Palm leaf' range	4.5"h	10-15			
3711.	Irish harp	4.5"h	8-12			
3712.	Ashtray square		2-5			
3713.	Condiment set and tray	8.5"l	15-20			
3714.	Vase 'Palm Leaf' range	6.75"h	15-20			

Mould No	Description	Size	Price Guide in £'s	Colour	Date Purchased	Price Paid
3715.	Plant pot 'Palm Leaf' range	6"h	15-20			
3716.	Bowl 'Palm Leaf' range oval		15-20			
3717.	Slipper vase 'Palm Leaf' range		8-12			
3718.	Bowl boat shape 'Palm Leaf' range large		15-20			
3719.	Bowl boat shape 'Palm Leaf' range small		15-20			
3720.	Vase 'Palm Leaf' range low	8.5"l	10-15			
3721.	Wall vase 'Palm Leaf' range		20-25			
3722.	Plant pot 'Palm Leaf' range	4.75"h	15-18			
3723.	Vase 'Palm Leaf' range		8-12			
3724.	Vase 'Palm Leaf' range	10"h	20-30			
3725.	Vase 'Palm Leaf' range	6"h	15-20			
3726.	Bowl oval 'Palm Leaf' range		10-15			
3727.	Jug on foot 1 pint		10-20			
3728.	Cream jug		8-10			
3729.	Cream jug 'Web' pattern		8-10			
3730.	Ashtray		2-5			
3731.	Vase 'Oslo' range	9.5"h	12-18			
3732.	Vase 'Oslo' range	8"h	12-18			
3733.	Vase 'Oslo' range	6"h	5-10			
3734.	Bowl 'Oslo' range large		10-12			
3735.	Bowl 'Oslo' range medium		8-15			
3736.	Bowl 'Oslo' range small		5-10			
3737.	Plant pot 'Oslo' range	4.5"h	10-15			

Mould No	Description	Size	Price Guide in £'s	Colour	Date Purchased	Price Paid
3738.	Plant pot 'Oslo' range	6.5"h	12-20			
3739.	Posy vase 'Oslo' range		5-10			
3740.	Vase 'Oslo' range	6.25"l	8-12			
3741.	Vase 'Oslo' range	9.25"l	10-15			
3742.	Mug baby size #	3.25"h	5-8			
3743.	Bowl 'Oslo' range	3.75"dia	8-12			
3744.	Bread and butter plate with butterfly		10-15			
3745.	Sandwich plate with butterfly	12.5"l	10-15			
3746.	Tea pot with butterfly		20-35			
3747.	Mug half pint 'Tudor' range		8-10			
3748.	Mug half pint		8-10			
3749.	Mug half pint embossed		8-10			
3750.	Mug as pineapple		10-12			
3751.	Mug		8-10			
3752.	Vase	10"h	18-22			
3753.	Jar		5-10			
3754.	Money box cat's head		50-90			
3755.	Bird	4"h	20-30			
3756.	Pie funnel bird's head	2"h	25-35			
3757.	Tea cup on foot		3-5			
3758.	Jar		5-10			
3759.	Plate fluted	10"dia	5-10			
3760.	Ashtray bowl		2-5			

Mould No	Description	Size	Price Guide in £'s	Colour	Date Purchased	Price Paid
3761.	Tray	15"l	5-10			
3762.	Horse		25-35			
3763.	Money box lifeboat man's head		50-90			
3764.	Jar square		5-10			
3765.	Dog Scottie sitting		45-75			
3766.	Dog Poodle sitting	6"h	45-85			
3767.	Dog Corgi sitting	6"h	45-85			
3768.	Triple tray		10-15			
3769.	Vase	10.5"l	18-22			
3770.	Money box cat's head		30-45			
3771.	Cheese dish oblong New 'Wishing well' range		15-20			
3772.	Honey pot New 'Wishing well' range		15-25			
3773.	Butter dish New 'Wishing well' range		20-30			
3774-3776	N/I					
3777.	Vase		10-15			
3778-3787	N/I					
3788.	Egg cup		10-20			
3789.	Stork	9"h	45-65			
3790.	Stork	6"h	35-55			
3791.	Baby plate nursery ware #	6"dia	15-20			
3792.	Vase		5-10			
3793.	Vase square		5-10			
3794.	Vase round large		15-18			

156

Mould No	Description	Size	Price Guide in £'s	Colour	Date Purchased	Price Paid
3795.	Vase round small		8-12			
3796.	Vase		8-12			
3797.	Vase		8-12			
3798.	Dog peke caricature		45-85			
3799.	Character jug lifeboat man		40-50			
3800.	Vase square		5-10			
3801.	Vase round		5-10			
3802.	Money box Seaman Jones small		25-35			
3803.	Lamp base 'Tudor' range	10"h	30-35			
3804.	Lamp base	9.75"h	25-30			
3805.	Lamp		25-30			
3806.	Bowl oblong	10.5"l	10-20			
3807.	Plant pot stone wall effect	5.5"h	15-20			
3808.	Plant pot stone wall effect	4.75"h	12-18			
3809.	Plant pot stone wall effect.	4.5"h	12-18			
3810.	Vase stone wall effect	10"h	15-20			
3811.	Vase stone wall effect	8"h	12-18			
3812.	Vase stone wall effect	6"h	8-12			
3813.	Bowl stone wall effect		8-12			
3814.	Twin vase stone wall effect	13"h	15-25			
3815.	Bowl stone wall effect	12"l	10-20			
3816.	Vase stone wall effect		5-10			
3817.	Bowl/Vase stone wall effect	14"h	15-25			

Mould No	Description	Size	Price Guide in £'s	Colour	Date Purchased	Price Paid
3818.	Tray stone wall effect	7"l	8-12			
3819.	Posy vase stone wall effect	14"l	5-10			
3820.	Posy vase stone wall effect small		3-8			
3821.	Bowl 'Glost' range	7.5"l	10-15			
3822.	Bowl 'Glost' range oval	11"l	10-12			
3823.	Bowl 'Glost' range large		10-20			
3824.	Vase bird shape 'Privet' range	5"h	15-35			
3825.	Vase 'Privet' range	7"h	12-15			
3826.	Bowl stone wall effect		8-12			
3827.	Dog slipper in mouth	5"h	50-75			
3828.	Coffee pot 'Avon' shape	8.25"h	15-25			
3829.	Dog Scottie		30-45			
3830.	Slipper stone wall effect		8-15			
3831.	Tray stone wall effect	13"l	8-12			
3832.	Jug		10-15			
3833.	Jar		5-10			
3834.	Jug 'Wisdom & Providence '	8.5"h	20-30			
3835.	Bowl		10-15			
3836.	Coffee pot		12-20			
3837.	Money box teddy bear policeman		50-90			
3838.	Bowl 'Manhattan' range		10-15			
3839.	Money box bunnies bank		50-90			
3840.	Money box cowboy		50-90			

Mould No	Description	Size	Price Guide in £'s	Colour	Date Purchased	Price Paid
3841.	Money box Indian		50-90			
3842.	Vase 'Privet' range	8.5"h	12-18			
3843.	Bowl and fish		25-35			
3844.	Vase 'Privet' range	10.25"h	18-22			
3845.	Vase 'Privet' range	6"h	5-10			
3846.	Bowl 'Privet' range oval	10"l	15-20			
3847.	Cat laughing	5.5"h	45-75			
3848.	Dog Scottie	4"h	30-45			
3849.	Fish on base		45-55			
3850.	Vase 'Linton' range	4"h	5-8			
3851.	Vase 'Linton' range	6"h	5-10			
3852.	Vase 'Linton' range	8"h	10-18			
3853.	Vase 'Linton' range		12-18			
3854.	Posy 'Linton' range		5-8			
3855.	Plant pot oval 'Linton' range	12"l	15-20			
3856.	Vase 'Linton' range		10-15			
3857.	Vase 'Linton' range large		15-18			
3858.	Pot 'Linton' range small		15-18			
3859.	Pot 'Linton' range large		10-15			
3860.	Bowl 'Linton' range small		10-15			
3861.	Bowl 'Linton' range large		12-20			
3862.	Posy slipper 'Linton' range		5-8			
3863.	Vase 'Begonia' range	4"h	5-8			

Mould No	Description	Size	Price Guide in £'s	Colour	Date Purchased	Price Paid
3864.	Vase 'Begonia' range	6"h	8-12			
3865.	Vase 'Begonia' range	8"h	10-15			
3866.	Vase 'Begonia' range	10"h	15-20			
3867.	Posy 'Begonia' range	7"l	8-12			
3868.	Plant pot 'Begonia' range		12-18			
3869.	Vase 'Begonia' range	4.5"h	5-8			
3870.	Vase 'Begonia' range large		12-18			
3871.	Pot 'Begonia' range		12-18			
3872.	Pot 'Begonia' range large		15-20			
3873.	Bowl 'Begonia' range		8-12			
3874.	Bowl 'Begonia' range large		10-20			
3875.	Slipper 'Begonia' range		5-8			
3876.	Tray 'Begonia' range		3-8			
3877.	Vase textured	4"h	5-8			
3878.	Vase textured	6"h	5-12			
3879.	Vase textured	8"h	10-15			
3880.	Vase textured	10"h	15-20			
3881.	Posy textured		5-8			
3882.	Plant pot textured		12-18			
3883.	Vase textured small		4-10			
3884.	Vase textured large		12-18			
3885.	Pot textured small		5-10			
3886.	Pot textured		5-10			

Mould No	Description	Size	Price Guide in £'s	Colour	Date Purchased	Price Paid
3887.	Bowl textured	6.75"l	8-12			
3888.	Bowl textured		10-20			
3889.	Bowl textured		5-8			
3890.	Tray textured		8-12			
3891.	Not used					
3892.	Cat smiling		50-95			
3893.	Tray 'Coral' range		8-10			
3894.	Bowl 'Privet' range		8-12			
3895.	Plant pot 'Privet' range small		12-18			
3896.	Plant pot 'Privet' range large		15-20			
3897.	Vase 'Coral' range	6"h	15-20			
3898.	Vase 'Coral' range		20-25			
3899.	Posy ring 'Privet' range		5-8			
3900.	Posy bar 'Privet' range		5-8			
3901.	Vase 'Coral' range	8"h	20-25			
3902.	Posy 'Coral' range		8-10			
3903.	Vase 'Privet' range oval	10.5"w	15-20			
3904.	Vase 'Coral' range	10"h	25-30			
3905.	Vase 'Coral' range oval		15-20			
3906.	Pot 'Coral' range		15-20			
3907.	Vase 'Coral' range	15.5"w	25-35			
3908.	Sugar bowl 'Avon' shape		5-8			
3909.	Cream jug 'Avon' shape		5-8			

Mould No	Description	Size	Price Guide in £'s	Colour	Date Purchased	Price Paid
3910.	Pot 'Coral' range		18-22			
3911.	Dish		5-10			
3912.	Squirrel		35-85			
3913.	Dog Jack Russell	3.5"h	25-35			
3914.	Egg cup 'Avon' shape	1.5"	3-6			
3915.	Bread and butter plate 'Lisbon' range		5-10			
3916.	Vase		5-10			
3917.	Vase		5-10			
3918.	Fox	5.5"h 6"l	45-85			
3919.	Mug half pint embossed	3.75"h	8-12			
3920.	Mug half pint		8-12			
3921.	Dog caricature	4"h	80-150			
3922.	Mug half pint		8-12			
3923.	Dog	2"h	50-90			
3924.	Vase on foot	10"h	15-20			
3925.	'Bambi' fawn		35-65			
3926.	Mug		8-12			
3927.	Fox plus chicken caricature	7"h	350-400			
3928.	Lamp base		20-30			
3929.	Vase tree with rabbits	9.75"h	65-75			
3930.	Bull 'Prestige Range'	14.5"l	100-125			
3931.	Jar	6"h	5-10			
3932.	Vase on foot	12"h	15-25			

Mould No	Description	Size	Price Guide in £'s	Colour	Date Purchased	Price Paid
3933.	Dog Pomeranian	4.5"h	40-60			
3934.	Pot 'Cactus' range	3"h	10-15			
3935.	Money box Squirrel	5.75"h	25-45			
3936.	Pot 'Cactus'	3"h	10-15			
3937.	Tankard 'Wisdom and Providence'	5"h	15-20			
3938.	Vase 'Manhattan' range	6.25"h	5-10			
3939.	Vase 'Manhattan' range	8"h	10-15			
3940.	Bowl 'Manhattan' range	6.25h	10-15			
3941.	Plant pot 'Manhattan' range	6.25"dia	15-20			
3942.	Plant pot 'Manhattan' range	5.75"dia	15-20			
3943.	Plant pot 'Manhattan' range	5"dia	10-15			
3944.	Vase 'Manhattan' range	7"l	5-10			
3945.	Posy 'Manhattan' range		3-5			
3946.	Vase 'Manhattan' range	8"h	10-15			
3947.	Vase 'Manhattan' range	10.5"h	12-18			
3948.	Tray 'Manhattan' range	12.5"l	10-15			
3949.	Bowl 'Manhattan' range large		10-2			
3950.	Tray 'Manhattan' range	6.5"l	5-8			
3951.	Posy 'Manhattan' range	5"l	5-10			
3952.	Posy 'Manhattan' large		5-10			
3953.	Ashtray 'Maple leaf' Montreal, Canada	5.5"dia	8-12			
3954.	Tankard 'Maple leaf' design		8-10			
3955.	Tray 'Maple leaf' design		5-10			

Mould No	Description	Size	Price Guide in £'s	Colour	Date Purchased	Price Paid
3956.	Vase 'Manhattan' range	11.5"l	8-12			
3957.	Fox		35-55			
3958.	Lamp base 'Hyacinth' range		20-30			
3959.	Lamp base textured	10"h	20-30			
3960.	Manx cat prowling prototype only					
3961.	Lamp base 'Macklestone' range		20-30			
3962.	Lamp base	12"h	20-30			
3963.	Extension to lamp 3962	8"h	5-10			
3964.	Vase wild pigs embossed	10"h	12-18			
3965.	Vase embossed	14"l	10-15			
3966.	Vase on three feet	9"h	12-20			
3967.	Vase on stand		12-20			
3968.	Dog Dachshund		45-85			
3969.	Vase		5-10			
3970.	Vase embossed	9.75"h	15-20			
3971.	Wall vase horse shoe		25-30			
3972.	Vase	4"h	5-8			
3973.	Mug		8-12			
3974.	Vase	5"h	5-8			
3975.	Tankard 'Wisdom & Providence'	4.25"h	15-20			
3976.	Lamp base 'Macklestone' range	10"h	15-25			
3977.	Cheese dish 'Totem' range		10-12			
3978.	Tankard 'Wisdom and Providence'	5.75h	15-25			

Mould No	Description	Size	Price Guide in £'s	Colour	Date Purchased	Price Paid
3979.	Lamp base 'Macklestone' range		20-30			
3980.	Vase		5-10			
3981.	Coffee mug		8-12			
3982.	Honey pot 'Totem' range	4.5"h	5-10			
3983.	Vase long		5-10			
3984.	Cat standing		45-95			
3985.	Coffee pot		15-20			
3986.	Butter dish 'Totem' range	6"l	10-20			
3987.	Posy 'Totem' range		3-5			
3988.	Dog Irish Terrier	5"h	30-45			
3989.	Pot		5-10			
3990.	Pot large		8-12			
3991.	Tray 'Tulip' range		5-8			
3992.	Vase		5-10			
3993.	Vase	6"h	5-10			
3994.	Vase 'Olympus' range	3.5"h	5-8			
3995.	Vase 'Maple' range	10.75"h	12-18			
3996.	Ashtray suede cover	5.25"dia	3-6			
3997.	Vase	8"h	12-18			
3998.	Urn 'Olympus' range	4"h	5-8			
3999.	Vase embossed	10"h	18-22			
4000.	Vase 'Olympus' range	6"h	8-12			
4001.	Vase 'Maple' range	10"l	5-12			

Mould No	Description	Size	Price Guide in £'s	Colour	Date Purchased	Price Paid
4002.	Plant pot 'Maple' range	5.25"dia	15-20			
4003.	Plant pot fluted		15-20			
4004.	Plant pot 'Maple' range	7"dia	15-25			
4005.	Pot stone wall effect	3.5"h	10-12			
4006.	Plant pot 'Maple' range	5.25"dia	15-20			
4007.	Bowl		10-15			
4008.	Vase 'Maple' range	7"l	8-12			
4009.	Ashtray suede cover		3-6			
4010.	Vase 'Maple' range	6"h	5-10			
4011.	Vase 'Maple' range	8"h	8-12			
4012.	Vase 'Manhattan' range	9"l	12-18			
4013.	Bowl 'Maple' range	7.5"dia	10-18			
4014.	Condiment set and tray 'Totem' range	3.5"h	15-20			
4015.	Bowl		5-10			
4016.	Posy vase		5-10			
4017.	Bowl round		5-10			
4018.	Bowl 'Maple' range	6.75"l	5-10			
4019.	Bowl 'Manhattan' range	4"dia	5-10			
4020.	Dish 'Totem' for fruit		8-10			
4021.	Coffee filter		3-8			
4022.	Oil and vinegar set on tray 'Totem' range		8-12			
4023.	Posy vase 'Maple' range		5-8			
4024.	Bowl 'Manhattan' range	8.5"dia	10-15			

Mould No	Description	Size	Price Guide in £'s	Colour	Date Purchased	Price Paid
4025.	Coffee filter.		10-15			
4026.	Sugar bowl		5-8			
4027.	Ashtray round	6.5"dia	3-5			
4028.	Coffee cream jug		5-10			
4029.	Toast rack 'Totem' range		5-10			
4030.	Cheese board and knife 'Totem' range		10-15			
4031.	Four egg cups on stand 'Totem' range		10-15			
4032.	Triple tray 'Totem' range	13"l	8-10			
4033.	Sugar bowl 'Totem' range	4"dia	3-8			
4034.	Beaker 'Totem' range		8-1			
4035.	Double tray 'Totem' range		8-10			
4036.	Sandwich tray 'Totem' range	13"l	3-6			
4037.	Coffee jug 'Totem' range	8.25"h	10-15			
4038.	Mug 'Totem' range	4"h	8-10			
4039.	Cream jug 'Totem' range	3"h	2-4			
4040.	Jug one pint 'Totem' range		5-10			
4041.	Storage jar large 'Nouveau' range		15-20			
4042.	Storage jar 'Nouveau' range small		10-15			
4043.	Jug 'Nouveau' range large		15-25			
4044.	Jug 'Nouveau' range medium		10-20			
4045.	Jug 'Nouveau' range small		8-10			
4046.	Tea pot 'Nouveau' large		15-25			
4047.	Tea pot 'Nouveau' range small		10-20			

Mould No	Description	Size	Price Guide in £'s	Colour	Date Purchased	Price Paid
4048.	Coffee jug 'Nouveau' range		10-15			
4049.	Cheese dish 'Nouveau' range		10-15			
4050.	Butter dish 'Nouveau' range		10-15			
4051.	Sugar bowl 'Nouveau' range		3-8			
4052.	Beaker 'Nouveau' range		8-10			
4053.	Sugar shaker 'Nouveau' range		8-10			
4054.	Honey pot 'Nouveau' range		8-10			
4055.	Mixing bowl 'Nouveau' range		15-20			
4056.	Mixing bowl 'Nouveau' range small		10-15			
4057.	Egg separator 'Nouveau' range		5-8			
4058.	Lemon squeezer 'Nouveau' range		5-8			
4059.	Condiment set 'Nouveau' range		10-15			
4060.	Vinegar bottle 'Nouveau' range		5-8			
4061.	Spice jar 'Nouveau' range	3.5"h	5-8			
4062.	Not used					
4063.	Vase 'Nouveau' range		8-12			
4064.	Vase 'Nouveau' range		8-12			
4065.	Mug		8-10			
4066.	Ashtray		6-8			
4067.	Coffee pot		15-20			
4068.	Vase acorn and squirrel	8.5"h	30-40			
4069.	Vase Stork	10"h	30-50			
4070.	Flower jug rabbit climbing	8.5"h	35-45			

Mould No	Description	Size	Price Guide in £'s	Colour	Date Purchased	Price Paid
4071.	Double egg cup		5-10			
4072.	Coffee filter		5-8			
4073.	Beaker		5-8			
4074.	Jam pot		8-10			
4075.	Honey pot 'Totem' range		8-10			
4076.	Coffee pot		15-20			
4077.	Cat Manx	3"h 4"l	50-70			
4078.	Pot square foot		10-15			
4079.	Urn vase		5-10			
4080.	Urn 'Olympus' range	6.25"h	10-15			
4081.	Urn 'Olympus' range	7"h	10-15			
4082.	Coffee percolator		15-25			
4083.	Pot square foot	11"h	15-18			
4084.	Urn 'Olympus' range	9.5"h	10-15			
4085.	Bowl square foot		8-12			
4086.	Bowl 'Olympus' range	10"dia	10-20			
4087.	Cream jug		5-8			
4088.	Sugar bowl		5-8			
4089.	Cream jug no handle	3.5"h	5-8			
4090.	Tankard fish		8-12			
4091.	Vase	8"h	12-18			
4092.	Vase	10"h	15-20			
4093.	Vase 'Olympus' range	8"h	12-18			

Mould No	Description	Size	Price Guide in £'s	Colour	Date Purchased	Price Paid
4094.	Lamp base 'Manhattan' range	10"h	20-30			
4095.	Tea cup 'Totem' range		3-5			
4096.	Vase	5"h	8-12			
4097.	Dog King Charles Spaniel	4.75"h	20-35			
4098.	Vase 'Olympus' range	10"h	15-20			
4099.	Coffee strainer		8-10			
4100.	Vase	12"h	15-25			
4101.	Coffee filter		5-8			
4102.	Coffee filter 'Totem' range		5-8			
4103.	Vase 'Olympus' range	5"h	8-12			
4104.	Bowl on square foot	7.5"h	12-18			
4105.	Vase 'Olympus' range	12"h	15-25			
4106.	Coffee pot 'Totem' range	6.25"h	20-25			
4107.	Bowl	7.5"dia	8-12			
4108.	Mug		8-10			
4109.	Bowl embossed	7.5"dia	8-12			
4110.	Vase horseshoe horse and shamrock	4.75"h	10-15			
4111.	Posy/ ashtray shamrock	6"l	2-5			
4112.	Candleholder	8"h	5-8			
4113.	Dog Great Dane	6"h	40-65			
4114.	Vase	8"h	10-15			
4115.	Bowl 'Olympus' on foot	7"h	10-15			
4116.	Vase seaweed and shells	8"h	12-18			

Mould No	Description	Size	Price Guide in £'s	Colour	Date Purchased	Price Paid
4117.	Vase floral	8"h	12-18			
4118.	Ashtray square	4"	2-5			
4119.	Vase	8"h	10-15			
4120.	Ashtray square	5.5"	2-5			
4121.	Vase 'Cornflower'	8"h	12-18			
4122.	Bowl square foot		10-15			
4123.	Bowl square foot small		8-12			
4124.	Jug one pint		15-20			
4125.	Ashtray golf		15-20			
4126.	Vase embossed	7.5"h	10-15			
4127.	Vase 'Sycamore' range	6"h	5-10			
4128.	Vase 'Sycamore' range	6.5"h	8-12			
4129.	Bowl 'Sycamore' range	8.5"dia	10-18			
4130.	Bowl 'Olympus' range	4"h	8-10			
4131.	Bowl 'Olympus' range	5"h	8-12			
4132.	Plant pot 'Hyacinth' range	7"dia	15-20			
4133.	Storage jar		5-10			
4134.	Tea pot 'Totem' range		15-25			
4135.	Tea pot		15-25			
4136.	Ashtray square		2-5			
4137.	Tea cup		2-5			
4137.	Bowl large		10-20			
4138.	Vase	6"h	5-10			

Mould No	Description	Size	Price Guide in £'s	Colour	Date Purchased	Price Paid
4139.	Jar spice		5-10			
4140.	Tea pot 'Totem' range		15-25			
4141.	Saucer 'Totem' range		1-2			
4142.	Breakfast cup 'Totem' range		2-5			
4143.	Jar storage 'Totem' range	7"h	5-10			
4144.	Tea pot 'Totem' range large		20-25			
4145.	Ashtray 'Totem' range	4"l	2-5			
4146.	Bowl 'Totem' range		8-12			
4147.	Bowl 'Totem' range large		10-12			
4148.	Jar spice 'Totem' range	3.5"h	5-8			
4149.	Cheese dish 'Totem' range	8.25"l	12-18			
4150.	Jar 'Totem' range large	8"h	8-12			
4151.	Egg separator 'Totem' range		5-8			
4152.	Vase 'Marina' range	8"h	10-18			
4153.	Plant pot 'Marina' range	7"dia	15-20			
4154.	Tray 'Marina' range	6.5"l	8-12			
4155.	Plant pot 'Marina' range	4.5"h	12-15			
4156.	Plant pot 'Marina' range	5.5"h	15-20			
4157.	Vase 'Marina' range	6.25"h	10-15			
4158.	Posy 'Marina' range	8"l	8-10			
4159.	Plant pot 'Marina' range	8.5"dia	18-25			
4160.	Vase 'Marina' range		10-15			
4161.	Bowl 'Marina' oval small		10-12			

Mould No	Description	Size	Price Guide in £'s	Colour	Date Purchased	Price Paid
4162.	Vase 'Marina' oval small		15-20			
4163.	Vase 'Marina' range	5"h	10-12			
4164.	Vase 'Flora' range	8"h	10-18			
4165.	Vase 'Flora' range	6"h	5-10			
4166.	Vase 'Flora' range	9.5"l	5-10			
4167.	Posy ring 'Flora' range	6" dia	3-8			
4168.	Vase 'Flora' oval large		12-18			
4169.	Plant pot 'Flora' range	5.5"h	12-18			
4170.	Plant pot 'Flora' range	4.75"h	10-15			
4171.	Bowl 'Flora' range		5-10			
4172.	Posy 'Flora' range long		5-8			
4173.	Bowl 'Flora' on tall foot		10-15			
4174.	Vase 'Flora' range	10"h	15-20			
4175.	Bowl 'Flora' range	9"dia	10-20			
4176.	Sugar shaker 'Totem' range		10-15			
4177.	Sauce boat and stand 'Totem' range		8-12			
4178.	Posy 'Marina' range		5-8			
4179.	Jug 'Totem' range 2 pint	6.25"h	15-20			
4180.	Coffee percolator		20-25			
4181.	Vase 'Knib' range		5-10			
4182.	Egg cups and stand 'Totem' range		12-15			
4183.	Tankard half pint		10-12			
4184.	Jar Hound head		8-12			

Mould No	Description	Size	Price Guide in £'s	Colour	Date Purchased	Price Paid
4185.	Sugar bowl Irish design small		5-10			
4186.	Cream jug Irish design		5-8			
4187.	Sugar bowl Irish design large		5-8			
4188.	Money box pig Irish design		20-30			
4189.	Mug		8-10			
4190.	Percolator Basket design		15-25			
4191.	Beaker		8-10			
4192.	Tankard leather cover		8-10			
4193.	Sauce boat and stand 'Totem' range		8-12			
4194.	Percolator basket design		15-25			
4195.	Tray round	6.5"dia	5-8			
4196.	Tray triangular		5-8			
4197.	Tray square	6.5"	5-8			
4198.	Tray oblong		5-8			
4199.	Vase crazy paving design	8.5"h	12-18			
4200.	Tankard could have pewter effect		10-15			
4201.	Plant pot 'Marina' range	4"h	10-15			
4202.	Coffee pot 'Totem' range	10.5"h	10-20			
4203.	Vase on foot		5-10			
4204.	Plant pot 'Marina' range	5"h	1-15			
4205.	Bowl 'Sycamore' range	6.5"l	8-12			
4206.	Vase 'Sycamore' range	8"h	8-12			
4207.	Vase 'Sycamore' oval		8-12			

Mould No	Description	Size	Price Guide in £'s	Colour	Date Purchased	Price Paid
4208.	Vase 'Sycamore' range	10"h	12-18			
4209.	Vase 'Sycamore' large		10-18			
4210.	Bowl 'Sycamore' range	5"dia	8-12			
4211.	Plant pot 'Sycamore' range	5.5"dia	8-12			
4212.	Plant pot 'Sycamore' range	6.25"dia	10-15			
4213.	Posy 'Sycamore' range		5-10			
4214.	Bowl low 'Sycamore' range	6"dia	8-12			
4215.	Vase 'Sycamore' range	6"h	8-10			
4216.	Sugar bowl		5-8			
4217.	Pot stand		3-5			
4218.	Covered bowl 'Agincourt' range	4.25"h	8-12			
4219.	Not used					
4220.	Jar 'Totem' range storage	6.5"h	8-12			
4221.	Plate 'Totem' range	10"dia	3-6			
4222.	Plate 'Totem' range	8"dia	2-5			
4223.	Plate 'Totem' range	6.5"dia	1-3			
4224.	Tea pot 'Totem' range	5.75h	15-20			
4225.	Lemon squeezer 'Totem' range		5-8			
4226.	Vase horseshoe embossed Welsh lady		8-12			
4227.	Vase horseshoe embossed Scottie dog		8-12			
4228.	Vase horseshoe Devon		8-12			
4229.	Vase horseshoe Cornwall		8-12			
4230.	Vase horseshoe Somerset		8-12			

Mould No	Description	Size	Price Guide in £'s	Colour	Date Purchased	Price Paid
4231.	Posy with deer 'Woodland' range		10-15			
4232.	Vase embossed		5-10			
4233.	Tree vase 'Woodland' with squirrel	4.5"h	10-15		APR '09	99p
4234.	Rabbit		20-25			
4235.	Coffee pot 'Totem' range		10-20			
4236.	Vase horse shoe Cheddar		8-12			
4237.	Percolator 'Totem' range	8.75"h	15-25			
4238.	Coffee percolator plain		15-25			
4239.	Posy with deer 'Woodland' range	2.25"h	10-15			
4240.	Basket with squirrel 'Woodland' range		10-20			
4240.	Basket with deer 'Woodland' range		10-20			
4241.	Tree vase 'Woodland' with squirrel	6"h	10-18			
4242.	Tree vase 'Woodland' with rabbit	9.25"h	20-25			
4243.	Twin tree vase 'Woodland' with rabbit	7"h	15-20			
4244.	Tray	7"l	8-12			
4245.	Tankard plain	4.5"h	9-15			
4245.	Tankard Hereford cider	4.5"h	15-25			
4246.	Ashtray horseshoe		3-8			
4247.	Lining	7"h	1			
4248.	Lining		1			
4249.	Tray with small figure		10-15			
4250.	Squirrel		15-20			
4251.	Dog Corgi	3"h	25-35			

Mould No	Description	Size	Price Guide in £'s	Colour	Date Purchased	Price Paid
4252.	Dog Peke pup similar to 3164	2.25"h	25-35			
4253.	Tankard 'Agincourt' range	3.75"h	8-12			
4254.	Tankard 'Agincourt' range	4.5"h	8-12			
4255.	Tankard 'Agincourt' range	5.5"h	10-15			
4256.	Beaker		5-8			
4257.	Beaker		5-8			
4258.	Vase		5-10			
4259.	Coffee jug 'Agincourt' range covered	13.5"h	15-25			
4260.	Mug embossed		8-10			
4261.	Lining	5"h	1			
4262.	Jam pot cauldron with pixie on lid	5"h	8-15			
4263.	Vase		5-10			
4264.	Vase 'Autumn Chintz' pattern	6"h	8-12			
4265.	Plant pot 'Autumn Chintz' pattern	5"h	10-15			
4266.	Vase oak leaves	8"h	12-18			
4267.	Tankard 'Agincourt' range	6.25"h	10-15			
4268.	Jug often pewter colour	5"h	10-15			
4269.	Honey jar embossed		8-10			
4270.	Tankard 'Agincourt' range	4.25"h	8-12			
4271.	Jug for cream 'Agincourt' range	4.25"h	8-12			
4272.	Jug 'Agincourt' range	6"h	12-15			
4273.	Tankard 'Agincourt' range	4.25"h	8-12			
4274.	Tankard 'Agincourt' range	3.5"h	8-12			

Mould No	Description	Size	Price Guide in £'s	Colour	Date Purchased	Price Paid
4275.	Tankard 'Agincourt' range	3"h	8-12			
4276.	Posy		5-8			
4277.	Vase	11"l	15-18			
4278.	Bowl		5-10			
4279.	Pot		8-12			
4280.	Bowl		5-10			
4281.	Posy vase	7"l	5-10			
4282.	Posy		5-10			
4283.	Mug		8-10			
4284.	Vase 'Collon No 1' large		25-30			
4285.	Vase 'Collon No 2' small		20-25			
4286.	Vase 'York'		20-25			
4287.	Plant pot with deer 'Woodland' range	4"h	10-18			
4288.	Ashtray with deer 'Woodland' range		8-12			
4289.	Bowl with squirrel 'Woodland' range	7.5"dia	10-25			
4290.	Twin tree vase Woodland' with deer	3.25"h	8-12		APR 09	99p
4291.	Plant pot and squirrel 'Woodland' range	5"h	15-20			
4292.	Bowl with rabbit Woodland' range		15-20			
4293.	Ashtray with deer Woodland' range	4.25"l	10-15			
4294.	Bowl oval		5-10			
4295.	Tankard 'Agincourt' range	5"h	9-15			
4296.	Tankard 'Agincourt' range	2.5"h	8-12			
4297.	Vase horseshoe embossed pixie	5"h	3-8			

Mould No	Description	Size	Price Guide in £'s	Colour	Date Purchased	Price Paid
4298.	Pot 'Harmony' range		8-12			
4299.	Vase 'Harmony' range	8"h	8-12			
4300.	Posy 'Harmony' range		4-8			
4301.	Vase 'Harmony' range	10"h	15-20			
4302.	Plant pot 'Harmony' range	7"dia	10-18			
4303.	Plant pot 'Harmony' range	6.25"dia	8-15			
4304.	Vase 'Harmony' range	10.25"h	10-18			
4305.	Vase 'Harmony' range small		5-10			
4306.	Vase 'Harmony' range	6"h	8-12			
4307.	Vase 'Harmony' range large		10-18			
4308.	Bowl 'Harmony' range		10-18			
4309.	Plant pot 'Harmony' range	7.5"dia	15-20			
4310.	Bowl 'Harmony' range	6.25"l	5-10			
4311.	Tankard 'Agincourt' range	5.5"h	9-15			
4312.	Honey pot		8-12			
4313.	Mug 'Totem' range		8-10			
4314.	Jam pot embossed		8-10			
4315.	Salt and pepper mustard 'Agincourt' range		15-20			
4316.	Ashtray Horseshoe Ireland	6"l	15-20			
4317.	Tankard 'Agincourt' range	4.25"h	8-12			
4318.	Tankard 'Agincourt' range	5.25"h	9-15			
4319.	Vase 'Aurora' range	8"h	15-20			
4320.	Vase	8"h	12-18			

Mould No	Description	Size	Price Guide in £'s	Colour	Date Purchased	Price Paid
4321.	Vase	8"h	12-18			
4322.	Vase	8"h	12-18			
4323.	Plant pot 'Aurora' range	5"h	10-15			
4324.	Plant pot 'Aurora' range	5.5"h	10-20			
4325.	Plant pot 'Aurora' range	6"h	10-20			
4326.	Plant pot 'Apollo' range	7.5"h	10-20			
4327.	Vase 'Aurora' range	6"h	8-12			
4328.	Vase 'Aurora' range	10"h	10-20			
4329.	Vase 'Aurora' range	4"h	5-10			
4330.	Vase 'Aurora' range oval	11"l	10-20			
4331.	Vase 'Aurora' range oval		12-18			
4332.	Bowl 'Apollo' range oval		8-12			
4333.	Percolator		10-20			
4334.	Pot 'Manhattan' shape		5-10			
4335.	Tray shell	6"l	3-8			
4336.	Bowl 'Harmony' range	4.25"dia	4-8			
4337.	Tray oval		3-8			
4338.	Plant pot 'Harmony' range	5"dia	8-12			
4339.	Coffee mug	4.75"h	8-12			
4340.	Vase 'Harmony' range	8"h	8-12			
4341.	Not used					
4342	Coffee mug embossed	3.75"h	8-12			
4343.	Coffee mug similar to 'Oslo' range	3.5"h	8-12			

Mould No	Description	Size	Price Guide in £'s	Colour	Date Purchased	Price Paid
4344.	Coffee mug		8-12			
4345.	Bowl 'Apollo' range		5-10			
4346.	Vase embossed		5-10			
4346.	Coffee pot 'Cordon Brun' range		20-25			
4347.	Vase		5-10			
4348.	Coffee mug embossed leaves	3.75"h	8-12			
4349.	Pot 'Olympus' range medium		10-15			
4350.	Pot 'Olympus' range small		8-12			
4351.	Pot 'Olympus' range large		12-18			
4352.	Tankard		9-15			
4353.	Number not used					
4354.	Tray shell on 3 feet		10-15			
4355.	Ashtray horseshoe horses head		5-10			
4356.	Plate 'Totem' range oval		3-5			
4357.	Plate dinner 'Totem' range oval		4-8			
4358.	Open jam pot		3-6			
4359.	Tray shell	6"l	8-12			
4360.	Money box Pig		20-35			
4361.	Money box Owl	4.5"h	20-35			
4362.	Mug 'Starway' range		8-12			
4363.	Pot		5-10			
4364.	Vase	6"h	5-10			
4365.	Vase	6"h	5-10			

Mould No	Description	Size	Price Guide in £'s	Colour	Date Purchased	Price Paid
4366.	Vase	6"h	5-10			
4367.	Vase	8"h	12-18			
4368.	Jug 'Agincourt' range	6"h	8-12			
4369.	Lining quarter pint		1			
4370.	Coffee pot		10-20			
4371	Vase	4"h	5-8			
4372.	Cup		3-5			
4373.	Vase		5-10			
4374.	Vase embossed		5-10			
4375.	Vase 'Riverside' range	8"h	20-30			
4375.	Posy vase 'Bamboo' range		5-8			
4376.	Pot		5-10			
4377.	Vase 'Riverside' range	6"h	10-25			
4378.	Coffee pot 'Starway' range	10.5"h	15-20			
4379.	Vase various ranges		5-10			
4380.	Pot		5-10			
4381.	Ashtray round	6"dia	2-5			
4382.	Sugar bowl		3-5			
4383.	Cigarette box rectangular		5-10			
4384.	Cream jug 'Starway' range	4"h	5-10			
4385.	Vase 'Riverside' range	4"h	15-20			
4386.	Beaker		5-8			
4387.	Tankard fish head	6"h	20-30			

Mould No	Description	Size	Price Guide in £'s	Colour	Date Purchased	Price Paid
4388.	Ashtray 'Evening Fantasy'	4.5"dia	2-4			
4389.	Jar tobacco		10-15			
4390.	Sugar bowl 'Starway' range	4"dia	5-8			
4391-4392	Not used					
4393.	Twin vase 'Riverside' range	3.5"h	10-15			
4394.	Bowl 'Riverside' range oval		15-25			
4395.	Candle holder 'Riverside' range	2.75"h	5-10			
4396.	Candle holder 'Hollyberry' range	2.5"h	10-15			
4397.	Ashtray square	4"	2-5			
4398.	Tray 'Hollyberry' range	8"l	15-20			
4399.	Tray 'Hollyberry' range	6"l	12-15			
4400.	Character jug 'Mine Host' large		30-50			
4401.	Character jug 'New Toby'	7.25"h	30-60			
4402.	Character jug 'New Toby'	5.25"h	30-50			
4403.	Character jug 'New Toby'	3.75"h	18-30			
4404.	Character jug 'Old Toby'	8"h	50-60			
4405.	Character jug 'Old Toby'	4"h	30-40			
4406.	Character jug 'Old Toby'	3"h	18-30			
4407.	Character jug 'Coachman'	5.5"h	50-60			
4408.	Character jug 'Coachman'	4"h	30-40			
4409.	Character jug 'Auld Mac'	4.5"h	30-40			
4410.	Character jug 'Auld Mac'	2.5"h	18-30			
4411.	Character jug 'Squire'	4"h	30-40			

Mould No	Description	Size	Price Guide in £'s	Colour	Date Purchased	Price Paid
4412.	Character jug 'Squire'	2.5"h	30-35			
4413.	Character jug 'Jolly Roger' medium		30-50			
4414.	Character jug 'Jolly Roger' small		18-30			
4415.	Character jug 'Gaffer'	3.75"h	18-30			
4416.	Character jug 'Gaffer'	2.5"h	18-30			
4417.	Character jug 'Fisherman'	2.25"h	18-30			
4418.	Character jug 'Nellie' small		18-30			
4419.	Character jug 'James' small		18-30			
4420.	Character jug 'Colonel'	3.25"h	18-30			
4421.	Character jug 'Silas'	3.25h	18-30			
4422.	Character jug 'King Neptune'	4.25"h	25-35			
4423.	Character jug 'King Neptune'	3"h	25-35			
4424.	Character jug 'King Neptune'	2"h	25-35			
4425.	Character jug 'King Neptune' V- large		40-60			
4426.	Character jug 'Santa Claus' V- large		40-60			
4427.	Character jug 'Santa Claus' large		25-35			
4428 .	Character jug 'Santa Claus'	3.25"h	18-30			
4429.	Character jug 'Santa Claus' small		25-35			
4430.	Character jug 'Mr Pickwick' V- large		35-60			
4431.	Character jug 'Mr Pickwick'	4.25"h	25-40			
4432.	Character jug 'Mr Pickwick'	3.25"h	18-35			
4433.	Character jug 'Mr Pickwick'	2"h	25-35			
4434.	Character jug 'Tony Weller' V- large		35-60			

Mould No	Description	Size	Price Guide in £'s	Colour	Date Purchased	Price Paid
4435.	Character jug 'Tony Weller'	4.5"h	30-35			
4436.	Character jug 'Tony Weller'	3.25"h	18-30			
4437.	Character jug 'Tony Weller'	2.25"h	18-30			
4438.	Character jug 'Sam Weller' V- large		35-60			
4439.	Character jug 'Sam Weller'	4.25"h	25-45			
4440.	Character jug 'Sam Weller'	3.25"h	18-30			
4441.	Character jug 'Sam Weller'	2"h	15-25			
4442.	Character jug 'Mrs Bardwell' V- large		35-65			
4443.	Character jug 'Mrs Bardwell' large		30-60			
4444.	Character jug 'Mrs Bardwell' medium		25-45			
4445.	Character jug 'Mrs Bardwell' small		20-35			
4446.	Character jug 'Mr Winkle' V- large		35-60			
4447.	Character jug 'Mr Winkle'	4.5"h	20-35			
4448.	Character jug 'Mr Winkle'	3.25"h	18-30			
4449.	Character jug 'Mr Winkle'	2.25"h	18-30			
4450.	Character jug 'Watchman'	4.5"h	20-35			
4451.	Character jug 'Watchman'	3.5"h	18-30			
4452.	Character jug 'Watchman'	2"h	18-30			
4453.	Character jug 'Cavalier' medium		60-90			
4454.	Character jug 'Cavalier' small		18-30			
4455.	Character jug 'George' medium		25-40			
4456.	Character jug 'George' small		18-30			
4457.	Character jug 'Simon'	3.75"h	30-50			

Mould No	Description	Size	Price Guide in £'s	Colour	Date Purchased	Price Paid
4458.	Character jug 'Simon'	2.5"h	25-40			
4459.	Character jug 'Mr Wolfe'	3.5"h	30-45			
4460.	Character jug 'Mr Wolfe'	2.25"h	18-30			
4461.	Character jug 'Mandolin Player' large		30-65			
4462.	Character jug 'Mandolin Player'	8"h	35-60			
4463.	Character jug 'Mandolin Player' small		18-30			
4464.	Character jug 'Louis' small		18-30			
4465.	Character jug 'Marie' small		18-30			
4466.	Character jug 'Charles'	2.75"h	18-30			
4467.	Character jug 'Cabby'	2.75"h	18-30			
4468.	Character jug 'Milady' medium		30-40			
4469.	Character jug 'Musketeer'	6"h	30-40			
4470.	Character jug 'Ann Hathaway'	5.25"h	30-40			
4471.	Character jug 'Ann Hathaway'	3"h	20-30			
4472.	Character jug 'Ann Hathaway' small		18-35			
4473.	Character jug 'William Shakespeare'	4.75"h	25-50			
4474.	Character jug 'William Shakespeare'	3"h	18-23			
4475.	Character jug small 'William Shakespeare'		18-30			
4476..	Character jug 'Churchill'	4.25"h	30-45			
4477	Character jug 'Welsh Lady'	3"h	18-30			
4478.	Character jug 'Shylock'	6.5"h	30-60			
4479.	Character jug 'Falstaff'	6"h	30-60			
4480.	Character jug 'Touchstone' large		30-60			

Mould No	Description	Size	Price Guide in £'s	Colour	Date Purchased	Price Paid
4481.	Character jug 'Romeo' large		30-60			
4482.	Character jug 'Juliet' large		30-60			
4483.	Character jug 'Irish Leprechaun' medium		25-50			
4484.	Character jug 'Duffy' medium		25-50			
4485.	Character jug 'Hamlet'		25-50			
4486.	Character jug 'Dick Turpin'	4.75"h	25-50			
4487.	Character jug 'Cavalier'	4.75"h	35-60			
4488.	Character jug 'Henry VIII'	4"h	25-50			
4489.	Character jug 'Yeoman of the Guard'	4.25"h	25-50			
4490.	Character jug 'Life Guard'	5"h	35-60			
4491.	Character jug 'William Shakespeare'	5"h	35-60			
4492.	Character jug 'George Bernard Shaw'	5.5"h	35-60			
4493.	Character jug 'Chelsea Pensioner'	4.25"h	25-50			
4494.	Character jug 'Grenadier Guard'	5"h	30-55			
4495.	Character jug 'Leprechaun'	4.5"h	18-30			
4496.	Character jug 'Fisherman'	5"h	25-50			
4497.	Character jug 'Harrods Doorman'	4.25"h	35-55			
4498-4499	Not used					
4500.	Tea pot Christmas pudding		30-45			
4501.	Mug 'Concord' range		10-12			
4502.	Three piece condiment on stand 'Concord' range		15-20			
4503.	Sugar bowl 'Concord' range		5-8			
4504.	Cream jug 'Concord' range		5-8			

Mould No	Description	Size	Price Guide in £'s	Colour	Date Purchased	Price Paid
4505.	Butter dish oblong 'Concord' range		3-5			
4506.	Cheese dish 'Concord' range		12-18			
4507.	Sandwich tray 'Concord' range		10-15			
4508.	Cup 'Concord' range		3-5			
4509.	Tray oval 'Concord' range	9"l	5-12			
4510	Coffee pot 1_ pints 'Concord' range		15-25			
4511.	Dinner plate oval 'Concord' range		5-10			
4512.	Coffee pot 2_ pints 'Concord' range		15-25			
4513.	Preserve pot 'Concord' range		6-10			
4514.	Plate 'Concord' range	8"dia	5-8			
4515.	Character jug Mrs Bardwell	S/S	18-30			
4516-4520	Not used					
4521.	Plant pot		12-18			
4522.	Tea pot		15-20			
4523.	Vase 'Rose' range	6"	5-10			
4524.	Ashtray 'Riverside' range	4.5"dia	3-10			
4525.	Cheese dish with cat and mouse	6.5"l	20-40			
4526.	Plant pot 'Rhapsody' range	6.5"dia	10-15			
4527.	Ashtray		2-5			
4528.	Vase with platform + figure	8.75"h	15-25			
4528.	Vase with platform & dog	8.75"h	25-40			
4529.	Vase 'Gossamer' range	7"h	10-15			
4530.	Honey pot 'Hollyberry' range	4"h	12-18			

Mould No	Description	Size	Price Guide in £'s	Colour	Date Purchased	Price Paid
4531.	Dolphin	8"h	30-50			
4532.	Vase		5-10			
4533.	Not used					
4534.	Vase	10"h	18-22			
4535.	Vase 'Privet' range	5"h	8-12			
4536.	Plant pot 'Privet' range	4"h	5-10			
4537.	Vase 'Privet' range	4"h	5-10			
4538.	Posy 'Privet' range		3-8			
4539.	Plant pot 'Privet' range	3.5"h	10-15			
4540.	Vase 'Privet' range	7"h	10-15			
4541.	Cream jug in shape of cow		25-35			
4542.	Vase 'Adam and Eve'	10"h	25-30			
4543.	Butter dish as a cow	7"l	15-25			
4544.	Bowl triangular		5-8			
4545.	Vase 'Spectrum' range	7.75"h	10-15			
4546.	Fox and stand with egg cups		100-150			
4547.	Bowl 'Riverside' range	10"dia	90-120			
4548.	Vase	8"h	12-18			
4549.	Face pot 'Apple sauce'	4.75"h	20-40			
4550.	Vase 'Tristan'	6"h	8-12			
4551.	Face pot 'Bread sauce' (number changed to 4557	4"h	40-65			
4551.	Vase 'Autumn chintz' range	M/S	10-20			
4552.	Vase	6"h	8-12			

Mould No	Description	Size	Price Guide in £'s	Colour	Date Purchased	Price Paid
4553.	Face pot 'Beetroot'	5"h	20-30			
4554.	Vase 'Rhapsody' range	8.25"h	10-20			
4555.	Vase 'Autumn Chintz' oval		10-15			
4556.	Vase 'Autumn Chintz' range	10"h	12-22			
4557.	Vase 'Autumn Chintz' range	8"h	10-20			
4557.	Face pot Bread sauce		40-65			
4558.	Vase 'Autumn Chintz' range	6"h	8-12			
4559.	Vase 'Autumn Chintz' range	10"l	12-20			
4560.	Posy 'Autumn Chintz' range		3-10			
4561.	Plant pot 'Gossamer' range	5.5"dia	12-20			
4562.	Plant pot 'Tristan' range		12-20			
4563.	Vase 'Tristan' range	8"h	10-20			
4564.	Vase 'Tristan' range		5-10			
4565.	Face pot 'Cucumber'	6"h	25-50			
4566.	Tankard fish head	5"h	25-30			
4567.	Tankard fish head	4.5"h	15-25			
4568.	Vase 'Evening Fantasy' range	8"h	10-15			
4569.	Urn 'Evening Fantasy' range	6.25"h	8-12			
4570.	Tankard skull	4"h	30-40			
4570.	Tea pot skull	4"h	25-35			
4571.	Percolator		15-20			
4572.	Sauce boat and stand 'Pisces' range		15-20			
4573.	Vase 'Assyria' range	8"h	10-20			

Mould No	Description	Size	Price Guide in £'s	Colour	Date Purchased	Price Paid
4574.	Tankard drinking horn	5.75"h	15-22			
4575.	Bowl 'Autumn Chintz' range	4.75"dia	8-12			
4576.	Cheese dish 'Hollyberry' range		25-30			
4577	Three piece condiment & stand 'Hollyberry' range		25-30			
4578.	Not used					
4579.	Posy 'Hollyberry' range		8-12			
4580.	Posy ring 'Hollyberry' range		10-15			
4581.	Vase 'Tristan' range	10"h	18-22			
4582.	Candle stick 'Hollyberry' range		10-15			
4583.	Pot 'Tristan' range		5-10			
4584.	Tankard boot shaped	5.75"h	15-25			
4585.	Salt and pepper duck		15-25			
4586.	Vase 'Tristan' range	6"h	5-10			
4587.	Jug with lid 'Starway' range	5.75"h	10-20			
4588.	Vase 'Tristan' range	6"h	8-12			
4589.	Posy bar		5-10			
4589.	Cheese dish cow		20-30			
4590	Bowl on foot 'Tristan' range round	5"h	10-15			
4591.	Bowl 'Tristan' range oval	6"h	10-15			
4592.	Vase	6"h	5-10			
4593.	Vase 'Tristan' range		12-20			
4594.	Vase 'Gossamer' range	9"h	12-20			
4595.	Vase 'Tristan' range		5-10			

Mould No	Description	Size	Price Guide in £'s	Colour	Date Purchased	Price Paid
4596.	Plant pot 'Gossamer' range	6.25"dia	15-20			
4597.	Vase 'Tristan' range		12-2			
4598.	Posy 'Tristan' range		5-8			
4599.	Vase 'Gossamer' range	5"h	8-12			
4600.	Butter dish barrel with cow on lid	5.25"dia	20-25			
4601.	Pot iron bound basket six feet 'Conway' range		5-10			
4602.	Vase	10"h	18-22			
4603.	Vase 'Gossamer' range	9.5"l	12-20			
4604.	Bowl 'Gossamer' range	4"dia	8-12			
4605.	Posy 'Gossamer' range		5-10			
4606.	Vase 'Gossamar' range small		5-10			
4607.	Vase oval		5-10			
4608.	Vase 'Rhapsody' range	6"h	8-12			
4609.	Vase small		8-12			
4610.	Vase	10"h	15-22			
4611.	Bowl	9.25"l	10-20			
4612.	Plant pot 'Rhapsody' range	5.75"dia	10-15			
4613.	Plant pot 'Rhapsody' range	8.75"dia	15-25			
4614.	Vase 'Rhapsody' oval large		10-20			
4615.	Vase 'Rhapsody' oval small		10-15			
4616.	Covered bowl 'Pisces' range		20-25			
4617.	Vase	10"h	15-22			
4618.	Vase	6"h	8-12			

Mould No	Description	Size	Price Guide in £'s	Colour	Date Purchased	Price Paid
4619.	Vase	8"h	10-15			
4620.	Bowl 'Rhapsody' range	9"dia	8-15			
4621.	Tankard		8-10			
4622.	Tankard Hound head		8-12			
4623.	Tankard Fox head		8-12			
4624.	Tankard Horse head		8-12			
4625.	Vase	6"h	8-12			
4626.	Vase	7"h	10-15			
4627.	Lochness monster souvenir		45-55			
4628.	Tankard drinking horn	8"h	15-25			
4629.	Vase 'Hollyberry' range	6"h	15-25			
4630.	Vase	6"h	5-10			
4631.	Vase 'Spectrum' range	6"h	5-10			
4632.	Tankard riding boot, 1 pint		15-25			
4633.	Mug 'Hollyberry' range	3.5"h	10-15			
4634.	Tray 'Hollyberry' range	9"l	20-25			
4635.	Bowl on foot 'Spectrum' range		5-10			
4636.	Vase 'Spectrum' range	10"h	15-22			
4637.	Plant pot 'Spectrum' range	6"dia	12-22			
4638.	Vase 'Rhapsody' range	10"h	15-22			
4639.	Comport 'Rhapsody' range	9"dia	10-15			
4640.	Plant pot 'Spectrum' range		12-18			
4641.	Bowl 'Rhapsody' range	5.25"h	8-12			

Mould No	Description	Size	Price Guide in £'s	Colour	Date Purchased	Price Paid
4642.	Posy 'Spectrum' range		5-8			
4643.	Vase 'Spectrum' range	6.5"l	5-10			
4644.	Plant pot 'Spectrum' range	3.5"dia	10-15			
4645.	Bowl 'Rhapsody' range large		8-12			
4646.	Vase 'Hollyberry' range	7.5"w	15-25			
4647.	Bowl 'Spectrum' range	5.5"dia	8-12			
4648.	Vase 'Spectrum' range	10"w	15-22			
4649.	Comport 'Spectrum' range	8.75"dia	10-20			
4650.	Badger	4"h	50-75			
4651.	Vase 'Spectrum' range	4.75"h	8-12			
4652.	Bowl 'Spectrum' range	7"dia	8-12			
4653.	Bowl 'Spectrum' range		8-12			
4654.	Vase	6"h	5-10			
4655.	Vase	6"h	5-10			
4656.	Vase	6"h	5-10			
4657.	Vase	6"h	5-10			
4658.	Vase	6"h	5-10			
4659.	Vase	6"h	5-10			
4660.	Vase oval small		5-10			
4661.	Vase	10"h	15-20			
4662.	Vase	10"h	15-20			
4663.	Vase	8"h	10-18			
4664.	Vase iron bound basket 6 feet. 'Conway' range	8"h	10-18			

Mould No	Description	Size	Price Guide in £'s	Colour	Date Purchased	Price Paid
4665.	Bowl 'Rhapsody' range	4.5"dia	5-8			
4666.	Bowl two handles 'Rhapsody' range		10-20			
4667.	Flower holder	6"h	5-10			
4668.	Cup 'Starway' range		2-5			
4669.	Salt and pepper 'Pisces' range		20-25			
4670.	Bowl round	3.5"h	5-8			
4671.	Posy ring	6.5"dia	5-8			
4672.	Posy horseshoe shape		5-8			
4673.	Posy bar	4.5"l	3-8			
4674.	Posy bar	6.75"l	5-10			
4675.	Posy bar	8.75"l	8-12			
4676.	Posy bar	13.25"l	10-15			
4677..	Posy tray		5-10			
4678	Plant pot 'Assyria' range	7"dia	15-25			
4679-4681	Not used					
4682.	Mug embossed owl		8-12			
4683.	Mint sauce boat on tray leaf design		8-14			
4684.	Plate 'Pisces' range	9.5"dia	15-25			
4685.	Plate oval 'Pisces' range	12.5"l	20-30			
4686.	Tea saucer 'Starway' range		1-2			
4687-4688	Not used					
4689.	Vase on foot	8"h	10-15			
4690.	Plate 'Assyria' range	12.5"dia	20-30			

Mould No	Description	Size	Price Guide in £'s	Colour	Date Purchased	Price Paid
4691.	Bowl iron bound barrel & handles. 'Conway' range		10-20			
4692.	Vase	6.5"h	8-15			
4693.	Vase 'Assyria' range	6.25"h	5-12			
4694.	Vase	6.5"h	8-15			
4695.	Vase	6.5"h	8-15			
4696.	Plant pot on three feet		10-15			
4697.	Plant pot on three feet		10-15			
4698.	Bowl on foot		10-15			
4699.	Plant pot 'Assyria' range	5.5"dia	15-20			
4700.	Preserve pot		8-12			
4701.	Vase	7"h	10-15			
4702.	Vase 'Etruscan' range	8"h	12-18			
4703.	Tray leaf		5-10			
4704.	Vase 'Assyria' range		5-10			
4705.	Plate 'Pisces' range	5"dia	8-12			
4706.	Plate 'Pisces' range	6.75"dia	10-15			
4707.	Horse and rider	9"l	90-130			
4708.	Pony and rider	6"l	65-90			
4709.	Hound lying down	4"l	40-60			
4710.	Hound sniffing	3.5"l	40-60			
4711.	Hound on all four	4"l	40-60			
4712.	Honey pot golf ball		20-35			
4713.	Honey pot foot ball		20-35			

Mould No	Description	Size	Price Guide in £'s	Colour	Date Purchased	Price Paid
4714.	Honey pot cricket ball		20-35			
4715.	Honey pot rugby ball		20-35			
4716	Honey pot tennis ball		20-35			
4717.	Honey pot hockey		20-35			
4718.	Honey pot bowls		20-35			
4719.	Tankard golf ball	3.75"h	25-35			
4720.	Tankard cricket ball	3.75"h	25-35			
4721.	Tankard football	3.75"h	25-35			
4722.	Tankard rugby ball	4.5"h	25-35			
4723.	Tankard tennis	3.75"h	25-35			
4724.	Tankard hockey	3.75"h	25-35			
4725.	Tankard bowls	3.75"h	25-35			
4726.	Tankard capstan sailing	4"h	25-35			
4727.	Tankard fishing	3.75"h	25-35			
4728.	Tankard soccer	3.75"h	25-35			
4729-4730	Not used					
4731.	Bowl on foot		10-15			
4732.	Bison	8"l	65-85			
4733	Buffalo	9.5"l	70-100			
4734.	Honey pot iron bound basket. 'Conway' range		8-12			
4735.	Tankard		8-12			
4736.	Tankard Thistle	3.75"h	8-12			
4737-4743	Not used					

Mould No	Description	Size	Price Guide in £'s	Colour	Date Purchased	Price Paid
4744.	Jug Maple leaf	4"h	15-20			
4745.	Jug Horse chestnut leaves	4"h	15-20			
4746.	Jug Oak leaves	4"h	15-20			
4747.	Jug Ash leaves with berries	4"h	15-20			
4748-4749	Not used					
4750.	Face pot 'Coleslaw'	4.75"h	80-120			
4751.	Face pot 'Tomato'	4.75"h	40-65			
4752.	Face pot 'Piccalilli'	5"h	80-120			
4753.	Face pot 'Chutney'	5"h	25-50			
4754.	Face pot 'Parsley'	4.75"h	90-120			
4755.	Face pot 'Pickled cabbage'	5.25"h	60-100			
4756.	Face pot 'Onion'	4.75"h	15-25			
4757.	Plant pot iron bound basket. 'Conway' range	5"dia	12-20			
4758.	Bottle	10"h	8-12			
4759.	Mint sauce boat		10-15			
4760.	Egg separator 'Humpty Dumpty'	4.5"h	60-100			
4761.	Bowl round. 'Conway' range	5"dia	8-12			
4762.	Bowl oval. 'Conway' range	7"dia	10-15			
4763.	Plant pot iron bound basket. 'Conway' range	4.25"h	12-18			
4764.	Plant pot iron bound basket. 'Conway' range		15-20			
4765.	Stand	3.75" dia	1-2			
4766.	Gnome large (not sold separately)					
4767.	Spirit measure 'Leather' range		5-10			

Mould No	Description	Size	Price Guide in £'s	Colour	Date Purchased	Price Paid
4768.	Dish thistles Scotland	6"dia	5-10			
4769.	Gnome	2.5"h	20-30			
4770.	Candle holder 'Chrys' ware		8-12			
4771.	Ice Jug no handle		8-12			
4772.	Vase 'Etruscan' range	6"h	10-15			
4773.	Vase 'Etruscan' range	5"h	8-12			
4774.	Bowl 'Etruscan' range	4"dia	8-12			
4775.	Vase 'Etruscan' range	4"h	5-8			
4776.	Plant pot 'Etruscan' range	5.5"dia	12-18			
4777.	Plant pot 'Etruscan' range	4.25"dia	10-15			
4778.	Plant pot 'Etruscan' range	6.5" dia	15-20			
4779.	Bowl 'Etruscan' range	10"dia	10-20			
4780.	Bowl 'Etruscan' range	6"dia	8-12			
4781.	Bowl 'Etruscan' on foot	7.5"dia	10-15			
4782.	Bowl 'Etruscan' on foot		8-12			
4783.	Bowl mini 'Etruscan' on foot	2.5"h	8-12			
4784.	Vase mini 'Rhapsody' range	2.75"h	8-12			
4785.	Jug mini.	3"h	8-12			
4786.	Vase mini.	3"h	8-12			
4787.	Vase mini.	3"h	8-12			
4788.	Jug mini	3"h	8-12			
4789.	Vase 'House in the Glen' range	8"h	20-30			
4790.	Twin vase 'House in the Glen' range	7"h	20-30			

Mould No	Description	Size	Price Guide in £'s	Colour	Date Purchased	Price Paid
4791.	Vase 'House in the Glen' range	6"h	15-25			
4792.	Moustache cup with handle		10-15			
4793.	Coffee pot 'Starway' range		15-20			
4794.	Moustache cup no handle		10-15			
4795.	Ice jug with handle		5-12			
4796.	Vase	10"h	15-20			
4797.	Coffee pot 'Medway' range	8.5"h	15-20			
4798.	Bird		20-25			
4799.	Vase		5-10			
4800..	Vase 'Bamboo' range	8"h	10-15			
4801	Mug 'Medway' range	3.75"h	8-12			
4802.	Sugar bowl 'Medway' range	3.5"h	5-8			
4803.	Vase	6"h	5-10			
4804.	Vase with Dolphin		15-25			
4805.	Vase	8"h	10-15			
4806.	Cream jug 'Medway' range	4"h	5-8			
4807.	Coffee pot 'Brazil' range	8.5"h	20-30			
4808.	Vase 'Bamboo' oblong		10-15			
4809.	Tea pot 'Croft' range	5.5"h	25-35			
4810.	Tankard embossed village	3"h	8-12			
4811.	Plate 'Croft' range	8"dia	8-12			
4812.	Honey pot 'Croft' range	4.5"h	20-30			
4813.	Cream jug 'Croft' range	3"h	15-20			

Mould No	Description	Size	Price Guide in £'s	Colour	Date Purchased	Price Paid
4814.	Sugar bowl 'Croft' range	3.5"dia	15-20			
4815.	Cheese dish 'Croft' range		25-30			
4816.	Butter dish 'Croft' range		25-30			
4817.	Mug 'Croft' range	4.5"h	5-10			
4818.	Tea cup 'Croft' range		5-10			
4819.	Saucer 'Croft' range		1-5			
4820.	Plate 'Croft' range	6.5"dia	8-10			
4821.	Plate 'Croft' range	8"dia	8-12			
4822.	Plate embossed cottage 'Croft'	6.75"dia	10-15			
4823.	Plant pot 'Fleur' range	4.75"h	12-18			
4824.	Vase oval 'Fleur' range		5-10			
4825.	Plant pot 'Fleur' range	4"h	10-15			
4826.	Vase oval 'Fleur' range large		12-20			
4827.	Vase 'Fleur' range	7"h	10-15			
4828.	Vase 'Fleur' range	5"h	8-12			
4829.	Vase 'Fleur' range	9"h	12-20			
4830.	Bowl 'Fleur' range on foot	5"h	10-15			
4831.	Thimble 'Croft' range in box		20-35			
4832.	Condiment set 'Croft' 2 or 4 piece		25-35			
4833.	Storage jar 'Croft' range	7.5"h	20-25			
4834.	Tea pot 'Croft' range	4.75"h	20-35			
4835.	Vase leaf with figure		15-35			
4836.	Stand with figure		12-20			

Mould No	Description	Size	Price Guide in £'s	Colour	Date Purchased	Price Paid
4836.	Stand with whisky tot		10-15			
4837.	Dog Spaniel small		25-30			
4838.	Two rabbits small		30-50			
4839.	Bull Galloway	2.25"h	20-30			
4840.	Vase and figure 'Privet' range		10-15			
4841.	Top hat with cat and dog		25-35			
4842.	Vase		5-10			
4843.	Tea cup 'Medway' range		3-5			
4844.	Tea saucer 'Medway' range		1-2			
4845.	Vase	6"h	8-12			
4846.	Dog St Bernard		40-60			
4847.	Gnome		40-60			
4848.	Bowl 'Bamboo' range		8-12			
4849.	Flower holder with picture frame		15-20			
4850.	Saucer leaf 'Brazil' range	5.5"dia	3-5			
4851.	Tea cup 'Brazil' range		4-7			
4852.	Sugar bowl 'Brazil' range	3.5"dia	10-15			
4853.	Cream jug 'Brazil' range	4"h	10-15			
4854.	Vase rock shape		5-10			
4855.	Vase 'Medway' range	5"h	8-12			
4856.	Vase 'Medway' range	5"h	8-12			
4857.	Vase 'Medway' range	5"h	8-12			
4858.	Vase 'Medway' range	7"h	10-15			

Mould No	Description	Size	Price Guide in £'s	Colour	Date Purchased	Price Paid
4859.	Vase 'Medway' range	7"h	10-15			
4860.	Vase 'Medway' range	9"h	12-20			
4861	Vase 'Medway' range	6"h	8-12			
4862.	Vase 'Medway' range	10"h	15-22			
4863.	Vase 'Medway' range	7"h	10-15			
4864.	Not used					
4865.	Preserve pot base	3"h	8-12			
4866.	Preserve lid Strawberry with 4865 or 4871		25-35			
4867.	Preserve Lid Blackberry with 4865 or 4871		25-35			
4867.	Preserve Lid Raspberry with 4865 or 4871		25-35			
4868.	Preserve lid Plum with 4865 or 4871		25-35			
4869.	Not used (Orange lid)					
4870.	Not used (Lemon lid)					
4871.	Preserve pot no lid leaf	2.75"h	3-8			
4872.	Horse Shire with harness		40-60			
4872.	Horse Shire no harness		30-40			
4873.	Tankard boot		10-15			
4874	Salt and pepper 'Medway' range		5-10			
4875.	Plate 'Medway' range	6.75"dia	3-6			
4876.	Preserve 'Medway' range	4.5"h	5-10			
4877.	Cheese dish 'Medway' range		8-15			
4878.	Dinner plate 'Medway' oval		4-8			
4879	Soup bowl 'Medway' range	5.5"dia	2-4			

Mould No	Description	Size	Price Guide in £'s	Colour	Date Purchased	Price Paid
4880.	Tea pot 'Medway' range		15-20			
4881.	Sandwich tray 'Medway' range		3-8			
4882.	Butter dish 'Medway' range		8-15			
4883.	Not used					
4884.	Vase	7"h	10-15			
4885.	Log with Blue tits		20-35			
4886.	Bowl 'House in the Glen' range	8"l	15-25			
4887.	Basket 'House in the Glen' range	5.5"l	15-25			
4888.	Tray 'House in the Glen' range	4.5"	10-15			
4889.	Posy round 'House in the Glen' range	8.5"dia	15-25			
4890.	Posy 'House in the Glen'		10-15			
4891-4894	Not used					
4895.	Face pot 'Lemon'	4.5"h	100-150			
4896.	Face pot 'Orange'	3.5"h	100-150			
4897.	Face pot 'Plum'		200-250			
4898.	Face pot 'Blackberry'	3.75"h	150-200			
4898.	Face pot 'Raspberry'	3.75"h	150-200			
4899.	Face pot 'Strawberry'	3.5"h	130-180			
4900.	Not used					
4901.	Cereal bowl		15-25			
4902.	Beef dripping holder	3.5"h	20-30			
4903.	Pork dripping holder	3.5"h	20-30			
4904.	Lard holder	3.5"h	15-25			

Mould No	Description	Size	Price Guide in £'s	Colour	Date Purchased	Price Paid
4905.	Soup bowl		15-25			
4906.	Face pot 'Pan scourer' lid	3.25"h	25-40			
4906.	Face pot 'Beef stock cubes' lid	3.25"h	25-50			
4906.	Face pot 'Chicken stock' lid	3.25"h	20-30			
4907.	Sink tidy bowl		35-45			
4908.	Soup bowl and lid embossed vegetables. Small size		20-30			
4909-4912	Not used					
4913.	Bowl for bath salts		8-12			
4914.	Mug fish		8-12			
4915.	Face pot 'Tartare sauce'	3.75"h	120-180			
4916.	Soap dish fish shape		10-15			
4917.	Toilet roll holder		8-12			
4918.	Talcum powder holder		8-12			
4919.	Tooth brush holder fish shape		10-15			
4920.	Not used					
4921	Plant pot hexagonal		15-25			
4922.	Plant pot hexagonal medium		12-20			
4923.	Plant pot hexagonal small		10-15			
4924.	Shaving tankard		15-25			
4925.	Shaving tankard		15-25			
4926.	Shaving tankard Sherlock Holmes		30-40			
4927.	Shaving tankard		15-25			
4928.	Rabbit used as additional ornament	2"h	20-30			

Mould No	Description	Size	Price Guide in £'s	Colour	Date Purchased	Price Paid
4929.	Pixie used as additional ornament		20-30			
4930.	Swan pomander		25-35			
4931.	Tea pot shape strainer and stand complete		20-35			
4932.	Vase		12-20			
4933.	Vase mushroom shape		12-20			
4934.	Vase mushroom shape	5"h	8-12			
4935.	Vase mushroom shape	6.5"h	10-15			
4936.	Vase		5-10			
4937-4944	Not used					
4945.	Ashtray coffin		10-15			
4946.	Vase	5"h	8-12			
4947.	Vase		5-10			
4948.	Vase	10"h	15-20			
4949.	Bowl		5-10			
4950.	Vase on square foot	7"h	10-15			
4951.	Basket etched floral		10-15			
4952.	Vase etched	8"h	10-20			
4953-4958	Not used					
4959.	Tankard		10-15			
4960.	Tankard		10-15			
4961.	Tankard		10-15			
4962.	Tankard		10-15			
4963.	Horse Shire	7"h	25-40			

Mould No	Description	Size	Price Guide in £'s	Colour	Date Purchased	Price Paid
4964.	Shaving mug	3.75"h	10-15			
4965.	Denture holder 'Mosaic' range	3"h	20-30			
4966.	Bath salts holder 'Mosaic' range		35-45			
4967.	Mug 'Mosaic' range	3.75"h	20-30			
4968.	Soap tray 'Mosaic' range		15-25			
4969.	Toilet roll holder 'Mosaic' range	4.25"h	25-35			
4970.	Tooth brush holder 'Mosaic' range	4"h	20-30			
4971.	Shaving mug 'Mosaic' range	4"h	20-30			
4972. 4839.	Tray/stand for Galloway bull Sold together		40-50			
4973.	Boy and dog not known					
4974.	Pomander chicken		15-25			
4975.	Pomander floral ball		15-25			
4976.	Bookends ships lanterns	5.75"h	60-80			
4977.	Kittens in boot	4.5"h	18-25			
4978.	Horse Shire	7"h	25-40			
4979.	Vase embossed basket		8-12			
4980-4985	Not used					
4986.	Dog Dachshund	7.75"l	25-45			
4987.	Basket	4"h	5-10			
4988.	Dog West Highland Terrier	6.25"l	30-50			
4989.	Pomander frog	2.5"h	15-25			
4990.	Pomander mouse		15-25			
4991.	Pomander squirrel		15-25			

Mould No	Description	Size	Price Guide in £'s	Colour	Date Purchased	Price Paid
4992.	Dog Boxer	5"h	45-60			
4993.	Vase 'Florence' range	4.75"h	10-18			
4994.	Vase 'Florence' range	4.75"h	10-18			
4995.	Vase 'Florence' grapevine	4.75"h	10-18			
4996.	Vase 'Florence' 2 handle	4.5"h	10-18			
4997.	Vase 'Florence' range	4.75"h	10-18			
4998.	Vase 'Florence' cottage	4.75"h	10-18			
4999.	Dog Spaniel standing		35-45			
5000.	Dog Collie	9"l	35-50			
5001.	Saucer embossed rose		1-3			
5002.	Cup embossed rose		3-5			
5003.	Vase 'Churnet' range	8"h	10-20			
5004.	Vase 'Churnet' range	6"h	8-12			
5005.	Plant pot 'Churnet' range	5"h	10-15			
5006.	Plant pot 'Churnet' range	5.5"h	12-18			
5007.	Vase 'Churnet' range	10"h	15-20			
5008.	Plant pot 'Churnet' range	5"h	10-15			
5009.	Bowl 'Churnet' range	7"h	12-18			
5010.	Plant pot 'Churnet' range	7"h	20-30			
5011.	Plinth for 5010 'Churnet' range not available					
5012-5014	Not used					
5015.	Vase 'Milton' range	8"	12-18			
5016-5018	Not used					

Mould No	Description	Size	Price Guide in £'s	Colour	Date Purchased	Price Paid
5019	Pot	7"dia 6"h	10-20			
5020.	Bowl		5-10			
5021.	Bowl	5"h	5-10			
5022.	Rose bowl and cover		10-20			
5023.	Dog Shetland sheepdog	6.25"h	20-40			
5024.	Dog Shetland sheepdog	7"h	25-45			
5025.	Dog Poodle sitting	11.25"h	75-125			
5026.	Vase	5.5"h	8-12			
5027.	Dog Yorkshire Terrier	5.5"h	25-35			
5028.	Posy log with Kingfisher		15-30			
5029.	Flower holder 'Pebble' range		10-15			
5030.	Tankard half pint 'Coco de Mer'		8-12			
5031.	Dog Poodle sitting	8.5"h	30-45			
5032.	Dog Boxer	7.5"l	35-50			
5033.	Jug embossed celery	7.5"h	25-35			
5034.	Dog Dalmation	9"l	35-50			
5035.	Horse hunter standing	11.5"h	65-80			
5036.	Money box dog		20-30			
5037.	Money box frog		20-30			
5038.	Tea bag holder	6"l	15-25			
5039.	Money box Owl	8"h	20-30			
5040.	Eagle		100-150			
5041.	Coffee bag holder	6"l	35-45			

Mould No	Description	Size	Price Guide in £'s	Colour	Date Purchased	Price Paid
5042.	Kitchen vase embossed spring onions	4.5"h	20-35			
5043.	Dish embossed corn on cob	9"l	10-20			
5044.	Container, triangular, resin made elswhere	-				
5045.	Container, fluted cone, resin made elswhere	-				
5046.	Container, plain cone, resin made elswhere	-				
5047.	Tea bag dispenser	10"h	20-30			
5048.	Face pot 'Horseradish'	4.25"h	120-200			
5049.	Dog Beagle	8.5"l	35-55			
5050.	Pie funnel swans		15-20			
5051.	Vase etched	6"h	5-12			
5052.	Thimble pigs head with box		20-25			
5053.	Thimble castle with box		20-25			
5054.	Thimble Rose with box		20-25			
5055.	Thimble Daffodil with box		20-25			
5056..	Thimble heart with box		20-25			
5057	Thimble Leaning tower of Pisa with box		20-35			
5058.	Thimble windmill with box		20-35			
5059.	Thimble circus clown with box		20-35			
5060.	Thimble 'Wishing Well' with box		20-35			
5061.	Thimble unicorn with box		20-35			
5062.	Thimble lion with box		20-35			
5063.	Cigarette box chest	4.25"w	10-15			
5064.	Ashtray		8-10			

Mould No	Description	Size	Price Guide in £'s	Colour	Date Purchased	Price Paid
5065.	Ashtray ships wheel		8-10			
5066.	Vase 'Trentham' range	5"h	5-10			
5067.	Vase 'Trentham' range	8"h	10-15			
5068.	Vase 'Trentham' range	5.25"h	5-10			
5069.	Plant pot 'Trentham' range	5"h	10-15			
5070.	Plant pot 'Trentham' range	6"h	12-18			
5071.	Vase 'Trentham' range	7.75"h	10-15			
5072.	Bowl 'Trentham' on foot	6"h	8-12			
5073.	Bowl 'Trentham' low round		8-15			
5074.	Dish/bowl 'Trentham' range		8-12			
5075.	Vase 'Trentham' range	4.25"h	5-8			
5076.	Dog Spaniel	7.75"l	30-45			
5077.	Coffee bag holder		25-35			
5078.	Tea cup		2-5			
5079.	Tea saucer		1-3			
5080.	Plate	6.5"dia	4-6			
5081.	Sugar bowl	3.25"h	2-5			
5082.	Cream jug	3.75"h	3-6			
5083.	Coffee pot	9"h	15-20			
5084.	Plate bread and butter	11"dia	10-15			
5085.	Sandwich tray	12.5"l	5-10			
5086.	Salt and pepper		8-12			
5087.	Tea pot	5"h	15-20			

Mould No	Description	Size	Price Guide in £'s	Colour	Date Purchased	Price Paid
5088.	Tea pot	5.75"h	15-25			
5089.	Cream jug individual		2-4			
5090.	Tankard	4.25"h	8-10			
5091.	Money box tortoise	5.75"l	25-35			
5092.	Money box owl	4.75"h	25-35			
5093.	Money box squirrel	5.75"h	25-35			
5094-5095	Not used					
5096.	Money box Bulldog	5.75"h	25-40			
5097.	Money box frog	5.25"h	25-35			
5098.	Tankard half pint		8-15			
5099.	Tankard moustache	3.75"h	10-15			
5100.	Pen tray		8-10			
5101.	Money box caricature tortoise		15-35			
5102.	Money box caricature elephant		25-35			
5103.	Money box caricature Bloodhound		15-30			
5104.	Money box with eyes Teddy bear without eyes		25-40 15-25			
5105.	Money box caricature Chipmunk		15-25			
5106.	Money box caricature owl		15-30			
5107.	Cat Siamese	8.5"l	55-80			
5108.	Dog Afghan hound	8.75"l	35-45			
5109.	Bowl cucumber		5-8			
5110.	Grapefruit bowl on stand		5-10			
5111.	Cat Siamese	8.75"h	50-80			

Mould No	Description	Size	Price Guide in £'s	Colour	Date Purchased	Price Paid
5112.	Dog Alsation	8.5"l	35-50			
5113.	Character jug 'Friar Tuck'	6.75"h	40-60			
5114.	Character jug 'Robin Hood'	6"h	40-60			
5115.	Character jug 'Sheriff of Nottingham'	6"h	40-60			
5116.	Character jug 'Little John'	6.75"h	40-60			
5117.	Character jug 'Maid Marion'	6.25"h	40-60			
5118.	Character jug 'Allan A Dale'	6.25"h	40-60			
5119.	Duck Mallard	6.5"l	70-80			
5120.	Duck Golden Eye	6"l	70-80			
5121.	Gosling		70-80			
5122.	Duck Shoveller	6.5"l	70-80			
5123.	Duck Tufted		70-80			
5124.	Mug		8-12			
5125.	Horse Shire	8.75"l	25-35			
5126.	Face pot 'Onion'	4"h	25-45			
5127.	Face pot 'Beetroot'	4"h	30-55			
5128.	Strawberry bowl		10-20			
5129.	Raspberry bowl		10-20			
5130.	Ashtray with cover		2-5			
5131.	Donkey		50-80			
5131.	Donkey with baskets or saddle		50-80			
5132.	Vase 'Florence' range	7.5"h	10-15			
5133.	Vase 'Florence' range	2.75"h	5-8			

Mould No	Description	Size	Price Guide in £'s	Colour	Date Purchased	Price Paid
5134.	Vase 'Florence' range	9"h	12-20			
5135.	Plant pot 'Florence' range	5.5"h	8-12			
5136.	Candle holder 'Florence' range		5-10			
5137.	Plant pot 'Florence' range	4.5"h	10-15			
5138.	Twin candle holder 'Florence' range	2.75"h	8-12			
5139.	Candle holder jug 'Florence' range	3.5"h	10-15			
5140.	Bowl 'Florence' on foot		8-12			
5141.	Not used					
5142.	Vase 'Florence' range oval		10-15			
5143.	Ham stand for Rodek		5-10			
5144.	Ashtray for Rodek		3-5			
5145.	Ashtray for Lesney with sand buggy		20-30			
5146..	Ashtray for Lesney with aeroplane		20-25			
5147.	Covered muffin dish and stand		10-15			
5148.	Jug and stand leaf for mayonnaise		15-25			
5149.	Pomander 'Mr Pickwick'		20-30			
5150.	Dog Dobermann	8.5"l	35-50			
5151.	Tray for banana split		10-12			
5152.	Elephant (5102) lamp base	5"l	40-60			
5153.	Ashtray (no number on base) with small deer		10-15			
5154.	Coffee mug series		4-8			
5155.	Coffee mug series		4-8			
5156.	Coffee mug series		4-8			

Mould No	Description	Size	Price Guide in £'s	Colour	Date Purchased	Price Paid
5157.	Coffee mug series		4-8			
5158.	Coffee mug series		4-8			
5159.	Coffee mug series		4-8			
5160.	Coffee mug series		4-8			
5161.	Coffee mug series		4-8			
5162.	Coffee mug series		4-8			
5163.	Coffee mug series		4-8			
5164.	Not used					
5165.	Bust Winston Churchill	8"h	100-120			
5166.	Rhinoceros	10.5"l	100-125			
5167.	Dog Labrador	9.5"l	25-45			
5168.	Butter dish sunflower lid	5"dia	15-20			
5169.	Butter dish oblong sunflower lid	6"l	15-25			
5170.	Dog Setter	9.25"l	40-50			
5171.	Coffee pot 'Alton' range		15-20			
5172.	Cream jug 'Alton' range	4"h	4-6			
5173.	Tea cup 'Alton' range		3-5			
5174.	Salt and pepper 'Alton' range		8-12			
5175.	Sugar bowl 'Alton' range	3.5"dia	3-5			
5176.	Tea saucer 'Alton' range		1-2			
5177.	Plate 'Alton' range	6.75"dia	3-10			
5178.	Teapot 'Alton' range	6.25"h	18-25			
5179.	Plate bread and butter	10.5"dia	8-12			

Mould No	Description	Size	Price Guide in £'s	Colour	Date Purchased	Price Paid
5180.	Butter dish 'Alton' range	5.25"l	10-15			
5181.	Cheese dish 'Alton' range		10-15			
5182.	Preserve pot 'Alton' range	4.75"h	5-10			
5183.	Cereal bowl 'Alton' range	6.5"dia	3-8			
5184.	Not used					
5185.	Bowl 'Dolphin' range	7.5"l	18-25			
5186.	Vase 'Dolphin' range	4"h	15-20			
5187.	Tray 'Dolphin' range		10-15			
5188.	Vase 'Dolphin' range	5.75"h	15-25			
5189.	Plant pot 'Dolphin' range	4"h	15-25			
5190.	Posy vase 'Dolphin' range		15-25			
5191.	Basket 'Dolphin' range		15-25			
5192.	Twin vase 'Dolphin' range	3.25"h	15-25			
5193.	Bowl	2.5"h	4-6			
5194.	Dog's bowl embossed head, bones etc. lid	5"dia	120-200			
5195.	Cat's bowl embossed head, fish etc lid	5"dia	120-200			
5196.	Vase		5-10			
5197.	Bull Galloway	5"h	60-80			
5198.	Character jug fisherman	5"h	30-50			
5199.	Character jug clerk	5"h	30-50			
5200.	Character jug horse dealer	5"h	30-50			
5201.	Character jug coal miner	5"h	30-50			
5202.	Character jug bricklayer	5"	30-50			

Mould No	Description	Size	Price Guide in £'s	Colour	Date Purchased	Price Paid
5203.	Character jug cook	5"	30-50			
5204.	Coffee mug	4"h	4-8			
5205.	Dog Welsh Sheepdog	9.5"l	35-50			
5206.	Character jug John F Kenedy	6"h	40-60			
5207.	Bull Galloway	4.75"h	60-80			
5208.	Mug with face of an orange	3.25"h	50-80			
5209.	Fox 'Prestige' range	10.5"l	45-80			
5210.	Gazelle 'Modus' range	9.5"l	60-80			
5211.	Squirrel 'Prestige' range	7"l	50-80			
5212.	Cheetah 'Modus' range	10"l	60-80			
5213.	Horse 'Modus' range	8.5"l	60-80			
5214.	Loving cup three handles		5-10			
5215.	Character mug 'George Washington'		25-50			
5216.	Badger with rock	5"h	80-120			
5217.	Tankard	4"h	4-8			
5218.	Tankard	4"h	5-8			
5219.	Tankard	4"h	5-8			
5220.	Not used					
5221.	Tankard Volvo		25-40			
5222.	Character tankard Indian 'Benskins' limited edition	5.75"h	80-110			
5223.	Vase embossed	8"h	10-15			
5224	Vase embossed	8"h	10-15			
5225.	Vase	8"h	10-15			

Mould No	Description	Size	Price Guide in £'s	Colour	Date Purchased	Price Paid
5226.	Vase	10"h	15-20			
5227.	Vase	7"h	10-15			
5228.	Vase	6"h	8-12			
5229.	Hippopotamus	6"l	30-40			
5230.	Camel	5"l	20-35			
5231.	Bear	6"l	40-50			
5232.	Two monkeys	4"h	30-45			
5233.	Lion	6.25"l	30-45			
5234.	Giraffe	5"h	30-45			
5235.	Cushion not available without cat					
5236.	Cat long haired	8.25"l	45-65			
5237.	Cat	11.5"l	45-65			
5238.	Polar Bear 'Modus' range	7"h	60-80			
5239.	Badger	5.5"h	100-150			
5240.	Plant pot	6.25"h	10-20			
5241.	Cup		3-5			
5242.	Holder for washing up brush	6"h	25-35			
5243 .	Flower jug 'Harvest Time' range	7.75"h	20-35			
5244.	Basket 'Harvest Time' range	6"l	15-25			
5245.	Plant pot 'Harvest Time' range	5"h	20-30			
5246.	Jug 'Harvest Time' range	4.5"h	15-25			
5247.	Twin vase 'Harvest Time' range	6"h	15-25			
5248.	Bowl small 'Harvest Time' range	5"l	15-30			

Mould No	Description	Size	Price Guide in £'s	Colour	Date Purchased	Price Paid
5249.	Bowl 'Harvest Time' range	6"dia	20-30			
5250.	Vase oval medium 'Harvest Time' range		20-30			
5251.	Mouse used as additional ornaments	2.5"h	– –			
5252.	Mouse used as additional ornaments	1.75"h	– –			
5253.	Not used					
5254.	Mouse used as additional ornaments		– –			
5255.	Fox used as additional ornament		– –			
5256.	Vase with mouse	6.75"h	20-35			
5256.	Vase with fox	6.75"h	20-35			
5256.	Vase with rabbit	6.75"h	20-35			
5257.	Rabbit used as additional ornament		– –			
5258.	Dog Great Dane 'Supreme' range	9"l	35-50			
5259.	Dog Schnauzer 'Supreme'range	7"l	35-50			
5260.	Dog Whippet 'Supreme' range	6"l	35-50			
5261.	Cat hunting	10.5"l	50-70			
5262.	Cat sitting	7"l	50-65			
5263.	Dog Poodle standing	5.5"h	30-55			
5264-5265	Not used					
5266.	Vase etched	7.25"h	10-15			
5267.	Vase	5.5"h	8-12			
5268.	Vase etched	7"h	10-15			
5269.	Vase etched	6.5"h	8-12			
5270.	Tankard half pint	4.25"h	8-10			

Mould No	Description	Size	Price Guide in £'s	Colour	Date Purchased	Price Paid
5271.	Tankard quarter pint	3.25"h	4-8			
5272.	Covered bowl plain	4.25"dia	5-10			
5273.	Bowl 'Rhapsody' range		5-10			
5274.	Bowl 'Vintage' range	7.75"dia	8-12			
5275.	Urn 'Vintage' range	9"h	18-22			
5276.	Plant pot 'Vintage' range	7"h	10-15			
5277.	Comport 'vintage' range	10.5"dia	10-20			
5278.	Vase 'Vintage' range	7"h	10-15			
5279.	Vase 'Bamboo' range		5-10			
5280.	Urn 'Vintage' range	9"h	12-20			
5281.	Tankard	5.75"h	10-20			
5282.	Tankard	8"h	10-20			
5283.	Tankard to fit holder quarter pint		12-18			
5284.	Tankard		8-15			
5285.	Leaf		5-10			
5286.	Face pot dishcloth	3.75"h	30-65			
5287.	Eagle	8"h	25-50			
5288.	Ashtray Geest		3-6			
5289.	Lop eared rabbit 'Thumper'	7"h	20-35			
5290.	Lop eared rabbit 'Thumper'	5.25"h	20-35			
5291.	Lop eared rabbit 'Thumper'	4"h	15-25			
5292.	Dog caricature	7"h	20-45			
5293.	Dog caricature	5.5"h	15-35			

Mould No	Description	Size	Price Guide in £'s	Colour	Date Purchased	Price Paid
5294.	Dog caricature	4"h	10-25			
5295.	Dog caricature	7"h	20-30			
5296.	Dog caricature	5.25"h	20-35			
5297.	Dog caricature	3.75"h	15-25			
5298.	Cat caricature	7"h	20-35			
5299.	Cat caricature	5.25"h	20-35			
5300.	Cat caricature	4"h	15-25			
5301.	Sheep dog caricature	7"h	20-35			
5302.	Sheep dog caricature	5.25"h	20-35			
5303.	Sheep dog caricature	3.75"h	15-25			
5304.	Dog Corgi	7.5"h	60-75			
5305.	Rabbit as 5289 Probably never produced					
5306.	Rabbit as 5290 Probably never produced					
5307.	Rabbit as 5291 Probably never produced					
5308.	Pot for tea bags	4.5"h	20-25			
5309.	Ashtray square	5.75"l	2-5			
5310.	Ashtray oblong		2-8			
5311.	Ashtray oval		2-5			
5312.	Dog Corgi		50-65			
5313.	Staffordshire Rustics 'Emily with dog'	10"h	70-95			
5314.	Staffordshire Rustics 'Alice with goat'		70-95			
5315.	Staffordshire Rustics 'Adam the Gamekeeper'		70-95			
5316.	Staffordshire Rustics 'Katie the Goosegirl'		70-95			

Mould No	Description	Size	Price Guide in £'s	Colour	Date Purchased	Price Paid
5317.	Candlestick	6"h	5-10			
5318.	Candlestick embossed	6"h	5-10			
5319.	Dog Chihuahua 'Supreme' range	5.75"h	30-50			
5320.	Dog St Bernard 'Supreme' range	9.5"l	35-55			
5321.	Dog Corgi 'Supreme' range	6.75"l	30-50			
5322.	Dog Old English Sheepdog 'Supreme' range	7"l	30-50			
5323.	Dog Sealyham 'Supreme' range	7.5"l	35-55			
5324.	Dog Pyrennean Mountain 'Supreme' range		35-50			
5325.	Jug 'New Cavalier' range	8"h	30-50			
5326.	Punch bowl 'New Cavalier' range	10.5"dia	20-30			
5327.	Wall plaque 'New Cavalier' range		20-30			
5328.	Tankard 'New Cavalier' range	5.75"h	18-25			
5329.	Jug 'New Cavalier' range	6"h	10-20			
5330.	Wine goblet 'New Cavalier' range	5"h	10-20			
5331.	Ashtray 'New Cavalier' range	5.75"dia	3-6			
5332.	Loving cup 'New Cavalier' range	5.25"h	20-30			
5333.	Tankard 'New Cavalier' range	4"h	8-12			
5334.	Decanter 'New Cavalier' range	9.75"h	15-25			
5335.	Hanging bowl 'Right Herbert'		25-45			
5336.	Hanging bowl 'Right Herbert' large		25-40			
5337.	Jug 'Cordon Brun' range	6.25"h	10-15			
5338.	Jug 'Cordon Brun' range	5.5"h	10-12			
5339.	Jug 'Cordon Brun' range	4.75"h	10-15			

Mould No	Description	Size	Price Guide in £'s	Colour	Date Purchased	Price Paid
5340.	Jug 'Cordon Brun' range	3.75"h	8-10			
5341.	Storage jar 'Cordon Brun' range	6.75"h	10-18			
5342.	Storage jar 'Cordon Brun' range	5"h	10-12			
5343.	Salt and pepper 'Cordon Brun' range		10-15			
5344.	Salt jar 'Cordon Brun' range	7.5"h	15-20			
5345.	Preserve pot 'Cordon Brun' range	4"h	10-15			
5347.	Tea pot 'Cordon Brun' range		15-25			
5348.	Mug 'Cordon Brun' range		8-10			
5349.	Butter dish 'Cordon Brun' range		10-15			
5350.	Cheese dish 'Cordon Brun' range	7.25"l	15-20			
5351.	Preserve pot holder 'Cordon Brun' range		2-4			
5352.	Tea cup 'Cordon Brun' range		2-5			
5353.	Tea saucer 'Cordon Brun' range		1-3			
5354.	Plate 'Cordon Brun' range	6.5"dia	3-6			
5355.	Plate 'Cordon Brun' range	8"dia	4-8			
5356.	Egg cup with saucer 'Cordon Brun' range		5-10			
5357.	Sugar sifter 'Cordon Brun' range	5.25"h	10-15			
5358.	Spoon rest 'Cordon Brun' range		8-15			
5359.	Egg separator 'Cordon Brun' range		8-10			
5360.	Lemon squeezer 'Cordon Brun' range		8-10			
5361.	Spice jar 'Cordon Brun' range	3.75"h	10-15			
5362.	Bowl 'Cordon Brun' range	6.5"dia	8-12			
5363.	Comport 'Cordon Brun' range	6"h	15-22			

Mould No	Description	Size	Price Guide in £'s	Colour	Date Purchased	Price Paid
5364.	Double egg cup 'Cordon Brun' range		8-12			
5365.	Teapot stand 'Cordon Brun' range		1-3			
5366.	Toast rack 'Cordon Brun' range		1-15			
5367.	Ashtray		2-5			
5368.	Ashtray		2-5			
5369.	Plant pot 'Bamboo' range	5.25"dia	12-18			
5370.	Vase 'Bamboo' range	7.75"h	10-15			
5371.	Plant pot 'Bamboo' range	6.5"dia	15-20			
5372.	Vase 'Bamboo' range	10"h	15-20			
5373.	Vase 'Bamboo' range	12"h	15-25			
5374.	Vase 'Bamboo' range	6"h	5-10			
5375.	Posy 'Bamboo' range	8"l	5-10			
5376.	Posy vase 'Bamboo' range	11"l	5-10			
5377.	Posy vase 'Bamboo' range	5.75"l	3-6			
5378.	Plant pot 'Bamboo' range	7.5"dia	15-20			
5379.	Plant pot 'Bamboo' range	8.75"dia	15-20			
5380.	Dog English Sheepdog	3.5"l	30-45			
5381.	Dog Skye Terrier	3.5"h	30-50			
5382.	Ashtray horseshoe		3-5			
5383.	Honey pot a bee	5"h	50-95			
5384.	Ashtray		2-4			
5385.	Pomander		8-10			
5386.	Tray 'Lincoln' range	7.25"l	2-5			

Mould No	Description	Size	Price Guide in £'s	Colour	Date Purchased	Price Paid
5387.	Vase 'Lincoln' range	8"h	10-15			
5388.	Jug 'Lincoln' range	8"h	12-18			
5389.	Plant pot handles 'Lincoln' range	5.75"h	15-20			
5390.	Bowl large 'Lincoln' range	12.5"l	12-20			
5391.	Vase 'Lincoln' range	10"h	15-20			
5392.	Vase	8"h	10-15			
5393.	Ginger jar 'Canton' range	11.5"h	30-40			
5394.	Ginger jar 'Canton' range	9.5"h	25-30			
5395.	Ginger jar 'Canton' range	7"h	20-25			
5396.	Jar 'Canton' range	13"h	40-50			
5397.	Jar 'Canton' range	9"h	25-35			
5398.	Covered bowl 'Canton' range	9"h	25-35			
5399.	Covered bowl 'Canton' range	9.5"dia	25-35			
5400.	Salt and pepper 'Severn' shape		8-12			
5401.	Jar for bath salts made for Boots	7"h	10-15			
5402.	Cheese dish 'Severn' shape	8.75"l	10-20			
5403.	Ashtray		2-5			
5404	Leyland lorry limited edition	4.5"h 9.5"l	150-250			
5405.	Ashtray		2-5			
5406.	Bowl	5"h	8-12			
5407.	Ashtray		2-5			
5408.	Tray		5-10			
5409.	Tea pot 'English Rose' range	5"h	15-20			

Mould No	Description	Size	Price Guide in £'s	Colour	Date Purchased	Price Paid
5410.	Sugar bowl 'English Rose' range	4"dia	3-6			
5411.	Cream jug 'English Rose' range	3"h	4-8			
5412.	Tea saucer 'English Rose' range	5.5"dia	1-2			
5413.	Plate 'English Rose' range	6.75"dia	3-6			
5414.	Tea cup 'English Rose' range	3"h	3-5			
5415.	Salt and pepper 'English Rose' range		10-15			
5416.	Preserve pot 'English Rose' range		8-12			
5417.	Cheese dish 'English Rose' range	7.5"l	10-15			
5418.	Butter dish 'English Rose' range	5.75"l	10-15			
5419.	Tea pot 'Severn' shape	5.5"h	15-20			
5420.	Jug No 4 'Severn' shape	4"h	5-10			
5421.	Mug	4"h	4-8			
5422.	Honey pot	5"h	8-12			
5423.	Tea Time set with clock face tea pot and mug		40-60			
5424.	Butter dish	5.75"l	10-15			
5425.	Tea pot 'Three Tea Bag Pot'	5.5"h	30-40			
5426.	Tea pot 'Two Tea Bag Pot'	4.75"h	20-35			
5427.	Tea pot 'One Tea Bag Pot'	4"h	20-30			
5428.	Tea pot stand	6"dia	20-35			
5429.	Jug No 3 'Severn' shape	4.5"h	8-12			
5430.	Jug No 2 'Severn' shape	4.75"h	8-12			
5431.	Lamp base owl	4.24"h	20-45			
5432.	Lamp base tortoise	3.5"h	20-45			

Mould No	Description	Size	Price Guide in £'s	Colour	Date Purchased	Price Paid
5433.	Lamp base hound	5"h	25-45			
5434.	Dog Springer Spaniel	8"l	30-45			
5435.	Jug 'Pipers Whisky' limited edition		20-25			
5436.	Ashtray 'Pipers Whisky' limited edition		10-15			
5437.	Ashtray 'Guinness' limited edition		10-15			
5438.	Bell with dove	5.75"h 4.5"dia	20-30			
5439.	Soap dish		8-10			
5440.	Ashtray tyre		4-8			
5441.	Jug & Teapot minature 'Hollington' range	3"h	15-25			
5442.	Jug miniature	3"h	10-20			
5443.	Jug miniature etched lines	3"h	10-20			
5444.	Jug miniature 'Hollington' range		10-20			
5445.	Jug miniature 'Hollington' range	3"h	10-20			
5446.	Jug miniature 'Hollington' range	3"h	10-20			
5447.	Honey pot 'Anniversary' range	5"h	5-10			
5448.	Goblet 'Anniversary' range	5"h	8-12			
5449.	Tea pot 'Anniversary' range	6.75"h	15-20			
5450.	Plate 'Anniversary' range	10"dia	8-12			
5451.	Trinket box 'Anniversary' range	4.5"l	8-12			
5452.	Cream jug 'Anniversary' range	3.75"h	3-6			
5453.	Tea cup 'Anniversary' range		2-5			
5454.	Tea saucer 'Anniversary' range		1-2			
5455.	Tea plate 'Anniversary' range	6.25"dia	5-10			

Mould No	Description	Size	Price Guide in £'s	Colour	Date Purchased	Price Paid
5456.	Loving cup 'Anniversary' range	7.5"dia	8-12			
5457.	Bowl 'Anniversary' range		3-5			
5458.	Ashtray 'Anniversary' range	5.5"l	2-4			
5459.	Candle stick 'Anniversary' range	6.75"h	8-12			
5460.	Bell 'Anniversary' range	5.25"h	10-15			
5461-5462	Not used					
5463.	Chicken egg cup, not used					
5464.	Chicken egg cup, not used					
5465.	Egg cup chicken shape		5-10			
5466.	Egg cup stand for four chickens	8"dia	15-25			
5467.	Yorkshire hod Ltd. Edition. Advertising John Smiths	10"h	50-60			
5468.	Cruet set 'Nessie'	13"l	80-120			
5469.	Jug 'Hollington' range'	9"h	18-25			
5470.	Jug with spout 'Hollington' range'	9"h	18-25			
5471.	Jug 'Hollington' range'	9"h	18-25			
5472.	Jug 'Hollington' range'	9"h	18-25			
5473.	Jug 'Hollington' range'	6.5"h	10-20			
5474.	Jug 'Hollington' range'	6.5"h	10-20			
5475.	Jug 'Hollington' range'	6.5"h	10-20			
5476.	Jug with spout 'Hollington' range'	6.5"h	10-20			
5477.	Not used					
5478 .	Egg cup truck 'Nursery Ware' #		50-70			
5479.	Egg cup steam engine 'Nursery Ware' #		70-90			

Mould No	Description	Size	Price Guide in £'s	Colour	Date Purchased	Price Paid
5480.	Jam pot Teddy bear #		50-95			
5481.	Vase hand painted 'High Tide' range	5.75"h	10-20			
5482.	Bowl 'High Tide' range	7.75"l	10-20			
5483.	Plant pot 'High Tide' range	4"h	12-18			
5484.	Plant pot 'High Tide' range	5"h	15-20			
5485.	Vase 'High Tide' range	7.75"h	15-20			
5486.	Vase 'High Tide' range	4.5"h	8-12			
5487	Basket 'High Tide' range	8.25"l	10-15			
5488.	Flower Holder 'High Tide' range	8.5"dia	10-15			
5489.	Bowl 'High Tide' range	5.25"l	5-10			
5490.	Vase Acorn		10-20			
5491.	Vase		5-10			
5492.	Vase		5-10			
5493.	Vase		5-10			
5494.	Vase		5-10			
5495-5498	Not used					
5499.	Vase 'Autumn Leaves' range	6"h	5-10			
5500.	Plant pot 'Autumn Leaves' range	6"h	5-10			
5501.	Jug 'Autumn Leaves' range	8"h	10-15			
5502.	Vase 'Autumn Leaves' range	10"h	12-18			
5503.	Covered bowl on foot 'Autumn Leaves' range	6.5"h	8-12			
5504.	Vase 'Autumn Leaves' range	11"l	5-10			
5505.	Plant pot 'Autumn Leaves' range	5"h	8-12			

Mould No	Description	Size	Price Guide in £'s	Colour	Date Purchased	Price Paid
5506.	Plant pot 'Autumn Leaves' range	7"h	15-20			
5507.	Trinket box 'Autumn Leaves' range	4"h 6"l	8-12			
5508.	Candle stick 'Autumn Leaves' range		5-10			
5509.	Jug 'Autumn Leaves' range	7"h	10-15			
5510.	Specimen vase		5-10			
5511.	Specimen vase		5-10			
5512.	Specimen vase 'Solo' range	4.25"h	5-10			
5513.	Specimen vase 'Solo' range	6.25"h	8-12			
5514.	Specimen vase 'Solo' range	4"h	5-10			
5515.	Specimen vase 'Solo' range	6.25"h	8-12			
5516.	Specimen vase 'Solo' corn cob	6.25"h	8-12			
5517.	Brooch/pendant dog Retriever's head		25-40			
5518.	Brooch/pendant dog Cairn's head		25-40			
5519.	Brooch/pendant dog Poodle's head		30-45			
5520.	Brooch/pendant dog Bulldog's head		30-45			
5521.	Brooch/pendant dog Spaniel's head		25-40			
5522..	Brooch/pendant dog Collie's head		30-45			
5523	Brooch/pendant horse's head		25-40			
5524.	Brooch/pendant horse's head		25-40			
5525.	Brooch/pendant horse's head		25-40			
5526-5528	Not used					
5529.	Salt and pepper beer mugs		15-20			
5530.	Money box beer mug		20-30			

Mould No	Description	Size	Price Guide in £'s	Colour	Date Purchased	Price Paid
5531.	Salt full beer mug		10-15			
5532.	Money box full beer mug		20-30			
5533.	Pot	4"h	5-10			
5534.	Not used					
5535.	Bell4.75"h 'Croft' range		8-12			
5536.	Jug 'Croft' range	7"h	15-20			
5537.	Coffee pot 'Croft' range	9"h	25-30			
5538.	Clock 'Croft' range	8"w	25-35			
5539-5546	Not used					
5547.	Honey pot clown		50-95			
5548.	Vinegar bottle 'Nosey Parker' face	5.75"h	50-60			
5549.	Pepper 'Nosey Parker' face	5"h	45-55			
5550.	Salt 'Nosey Parker' face	4.75"h	45-55			
5551.	Tray for plant pots		5-8			
5552.	Tray for plant pots		5-8			
5553.	Cradle	3.5"h	45-90			
5554.	Pair of baby boots	3.5"h	40-80			
5555.	Stork carrying bundle	4.5"h	25-35			
5556-5558	Not used					
5559.	Wall plaque miniature	4.25"dia	10-15			
5560.	Wall plaque miniature	3.5"dia	10-15			
5561-5562	Not used					
5563.	Tray		8-10			

Mould No	Description	Size	Price Guide in £'s	Colour	Date Purchased	Price Paid
5564.	Toilet roll holder		5-8			
5565.	Covered jar for bath salts		10-15			
5566.	Tooth brush holder		10-15			
5567.	Bowl for dentures		10-15			
5568-5570	Not used					
5571.	Plant pot 'Giant Panda' range	4.5"h	20-30			
5572.	Twin vase 'Giant Panda' range	6.25"h	20-35			
5573.	Jug 'Giant Panda' range	9"h	30-40			
5574.	Jug 'Giant Panda' range	7.5"h	20-30			
5575.	Bowl 'Giant Panda' range		20-30			
5576.	Money box 'Giant Panda' range	4.25"h	35-50			
5577.	Not produced 'Giant Panda' range					
5578.	Panda sitting 'Giant Panda' range	2.25"h	20-30			
5579.	Panda standing 'Giant Panda' range	1.5"h	20-30			
5580.	Disc small		10-15			
5581.	Disc large		10-15			
5582.	Martingale three discs on leather	16.5"l	20-25			
5583.	Martingale three discs on leather	25"l	20-25			
5584.	Trinket box 'Milady' range	5.25"l	8-12			
5585.	Ring stand 'Milady' range	4.5"dia	4-6			
5586.	Plant pot 'Milady' range	6.75"dia	15-25			
5587.	Tray 'Milady' range	10"l	5-10			
5588.	Covered bowl 'Milady' range	4.5"dia	8-12			

Mould No	Description	Size	Price Guide in £'s	Colour	Date Purchased	Price Paid
5589.	Candle stick 'Milady' range	4"h	4-6			
5590.	Plant pot 'Milady' range	5.5"dia	15-20			
5591.	Plant pot 'Milady' range	4.75"dia	12-18			
5592.	Vase 'Milady' range	8"h	12-18			
5593.	Vase 'Milady' range	6"h	8-12			
5594.	Hand mirror 'Milady' range	8.75"l	15-25			
5595.	Specimen vase 'Milady' range	6.75"h	8-12			
5596.	Vase '1904' range	8.5"h	15-25			
5597.	Jug '1904' range	9"h	15-25			
5598.	Vase '1904' range	9.5"h	15-25			
5599.	Vase '1904' range	9.25"h	15-25			
5600.	Vase '1904' range	9"h	15-25			
5601-5605	Not used					
5606.	Vase 'Belgravia' range	8.25"h	10-20			
5607.	Vase 'Belgravia' range	6.75"h	10-15			
5608.	Vase 'Belgravia' range	6"h	5-10			
5609.	Vase 'Belgravia' range	6.25"l	5-10			
5610.	Bowl 'Belgravia' range	7.75"l	8-12			
5611.	Plant pot 'Belgravia' range	4.5"h	10-15			
5612.	Plant pot 'Belgravia' range	5"h	10-15			
5613.	Plant pot 'Belgravia' range	5.5"h	12-18			
5614.	Plant pot 'Belgravia' range	6.5"h	15-20			
5615.	Plant pot 'Belgravia' range	7.5"h	15-25			

Mould No	Description	Size	Price Guide in £'s	Colour	Date Purchased	Price Paid
5616-5619	Not used					
5620.	Tea cup 'Tapestry' range	3"h	3-5			
5621.	Tea saucer 'Tapestry' range	5.75"dia	1-2			
5622.	Tea plate 'Tapestry' range	6.5"dia	4-6			
5623.	Mug 'Tapestry' range	4.5"h	4-8			
5624.	Sugar bowl 'Tapestry' range	3.25"dia	3-5			
5625.	Cream jug 'Tapestry' range	3.5"h	4-8			
5626.	Tea pot 'Tapestry' range	5"h	15-20			
5627.	Sandwich tray 'Tapestry' range	11.75"l	5-8			
5628.	Salt and pepper 'Tapestry' range	3.5"h	8-12			
5629.	Butter dish 'Tapestry' range	5.25"l	12-20			
5630.	Cheese dish 'Tapestry' range	7.5"l	12-20			
5631.	Preserve pot 'Tapestry' range	3.5"h	8-10			
5632-5633	Not used					
5634.	Tea pot large		20-25			
5635.	Tea pot large		20-25			
5636.	Tea pot small		15-20			
5637.	Tea pot small		15-20			
5638-5643	Not used					
5644.	Thimble wedding cake ,with box		20-25			
5645-5654	Not used					
5655.	Mug pig		25-40			
5656.	Money box bear	5.25"h	35-50			

Mould No	Description	Size	Price Guide in £'s	Colour	Date Purchased	Price Paid
5657.	Money box pig	5.5"h	35-50			
5658.	Money box rabbit	5.75"h	40-55			
5659.	Money box elephant	5.75"h	40-55			
5660.	Money box Cheshire cat	6.25"l	50-80			
5661..	Money box Bassett hound	5.5"h	35-50			
5662	Money box fish	6.5"l	50-80			
5663-5669	Not used					
5670.	Tea pot 'Tudor Cottage' range	5.5"h	20-35			
5671.	Sugar bowl 'Tudor Cottage' range	3"dia	15-20			
5672	Cream jug 'Tudor Cottage' range	3.25"h	15-20			
5673.	Butter dish 'Tudor Cottage' range	5.75"l	25-30			
5674.	Cheese dish 'Tudor Cottage' range	7"l	25-30			
5675.	Preserve pot 'Tudor Cottage' range	4.5"h	20-30			
5676.	Salt and pepper 'Tudor Cottage' range	3.25"h	15-25			
5677-5995	Not used					
5996..	Newspaper holder 'Desk Top' range	4.5"h	25-35			
5997	Match box tray 'Desk Top' range	5.25"l	15-20			
5998.	Match box pen holder 'Desk Top' range	4"h	18-25			
5999.	Sack pen holder 'Desk Top' range	4.25"h	25-30			
6000.	Scrap paper tray 'Desk Top' range	5.25"l	20-25			
6001.	Box gift wrapped 'Desk Top' range	4.25"l	15-25			
6002.	Carrier bag pen holder 'Desk Top' range	4"h	10-20			
6002.	Carrier bag pen holder for Harrods	4"h	25-30			

Mould No	Description	Size	Price Guide in £'s	Colour	Date Purchased	Price Paid
6003.	Money box parcel 'Desk Top' range	4"l	20-30			
6004.	Paper weight 'Desk Top' range		18-25			
6005.	Ball of string dispenser 'Desk Top' range	3.75"h	18-25			
6006.	Beer can		15-20			
6007.	Not used					
6008.	Tray 'Desk Top' range	5.25"l	15-25			
6009-6127	Not used					
6128.	Money box letter 'P'	5.25"h	25-30			

FACTORY CEASED PRODUCTION

Particular patterns decorated on 'Avon' shapes will command higher prices. For example nursery ware: Zoo line, Teddy.

Mould No	Description	Size	Price Guide in £'s	Colour	Date Purchased	Price Paid
3262.	Plate	8"dia	12-18			
3263.	Plate	6.5"dia	10.14			
3264.	Bowl	6.25"dia	10-16			
3617.	Baby mug 2 handle		20-30			
3742.	Mug		15-25			
3788.	Egg cup		10-20			
3791.	Baby plate		15-20			
5478.	Egg cup engine trailer		15-70			
5479.	Engine		50-70			
5480.	Jam pot - teddy bear (not nursery ware)	5.5"	20-40			

Falcon ware Numbers have prefix 'F' and are unrelated to old Shaw and Copestake Numbers

THE
SYLVAC

Illustrated
COLLECTORS HANDBOOK

Please Help

Dear Reader,

I am looking for collectors willing to help build up our library of pictures for future editions of this book. Although we have hundreds of photos we still need more. Our aim is to produce the best pictorial price guide on the market for all collectors, a large task but one I hope will benefit all Sylvac enthusiasts.

If you can help we can do it without fuss. We will visit you with the photographic equipment by prior arrangement.

If you think you would like to help please write to me.

Anthony Van Der Woerd
Georgian Publication
PO BOX 1449
Bath
BA1 2FF

Our web site is Sylvac.org

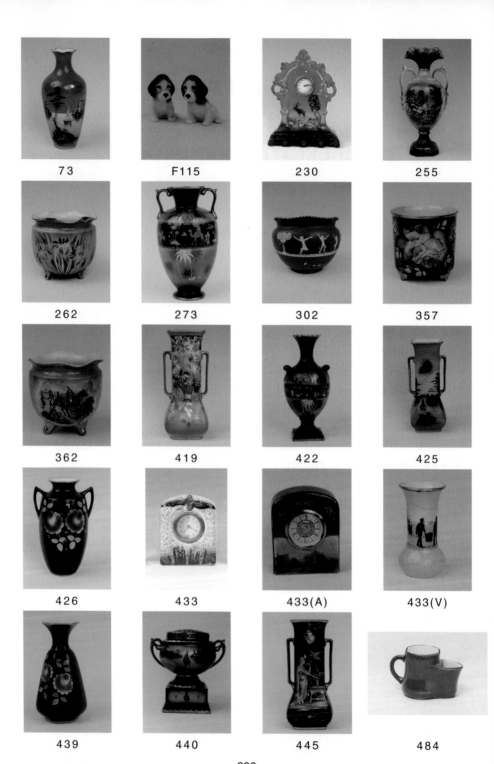

73

F115

230

255

262

273

302

357

362

419

422

425

426

433

433(A)

433(V)

439

440

445

484

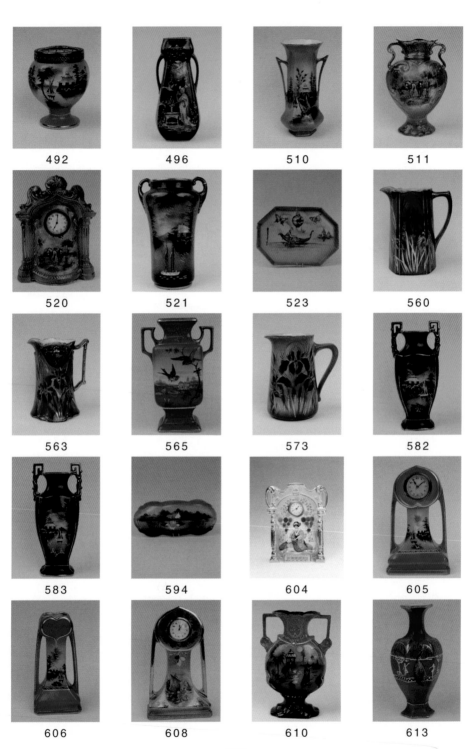

492 496 510 511

520 521 523 560

563 565 573 582

583 594 604 605

606 608 610 613

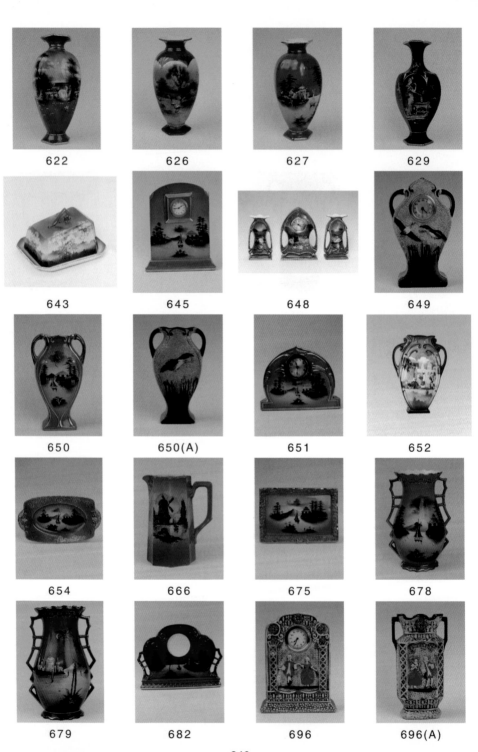

622

626

627

629

643

645

648

649

650

650(A)

651

652

654

666

675

678

679

682

696

696(A)

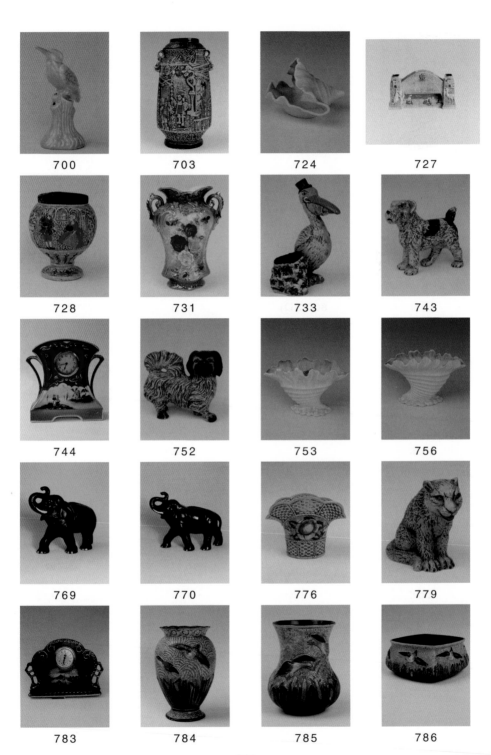

700 703 724 727

728 731 733 743

744 752 753 756

769 770 776 779

783 784 785 786

787 788 789 793

805 809(SQ) 813 814

815 821 822 823

829 832 833 839

840 842 843 844

845   847   848   858

858.1   861   862   864

865   869   871   880

881   887   888   890

893   898   902   903

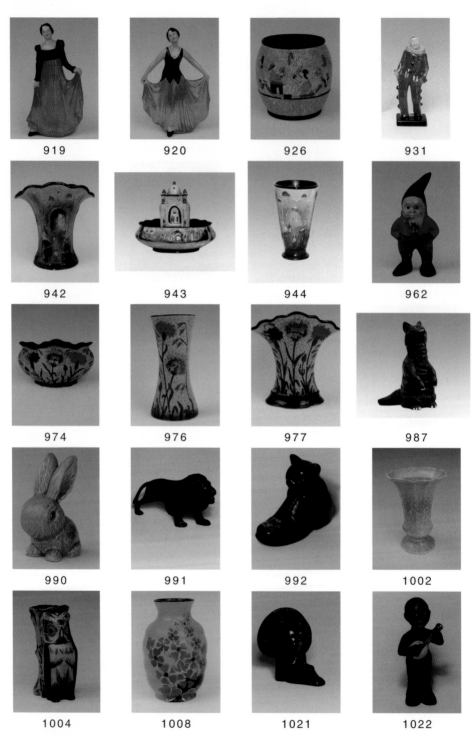

919

920

926

931

942

943

944

962

974

976

977

987

990

991

992

1002

1004

1008

1021

1022

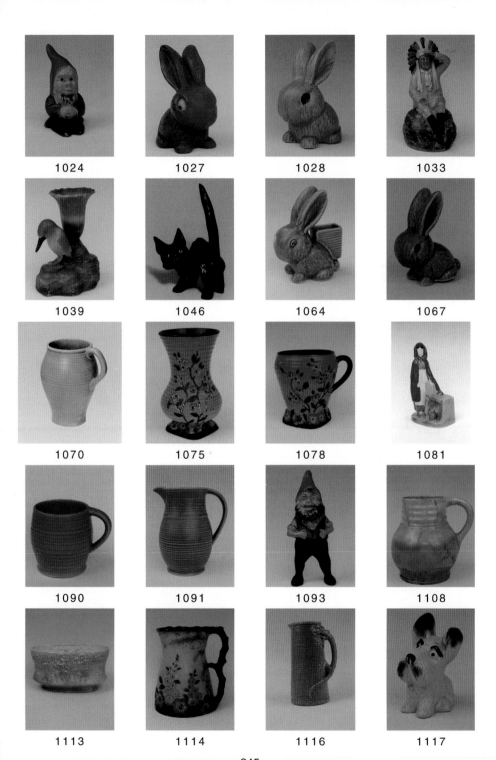

1024

1027

1028

1033

1039

1046

1064

1067

1070

1075

1078

1081

1090

1091

1093

1108

1113

1114

1116

1117

1118   1119   1120   1121

1122   1125   1132   1134

1138   1143   1148   1153

1157   1167   1173   1175

1183   1190   1196   1201

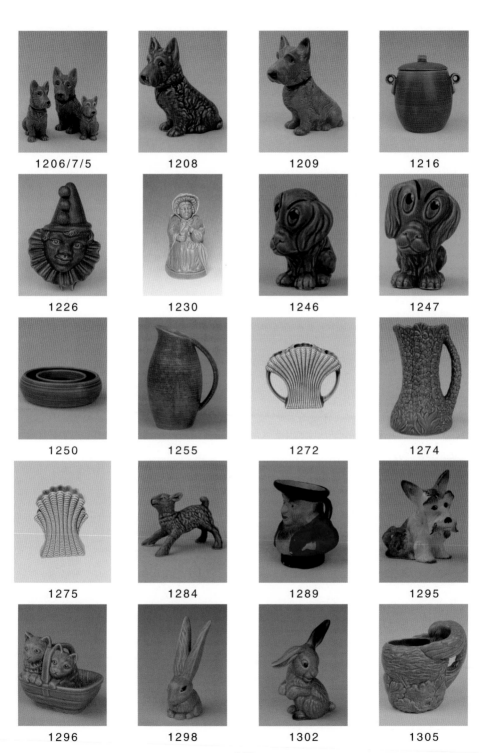

1206/7/5   1208   1209   1216

1226   1230   1246   1247

1250   1255   1272   1274

1275   1284   1289   1295

1296   1298   1302   1305

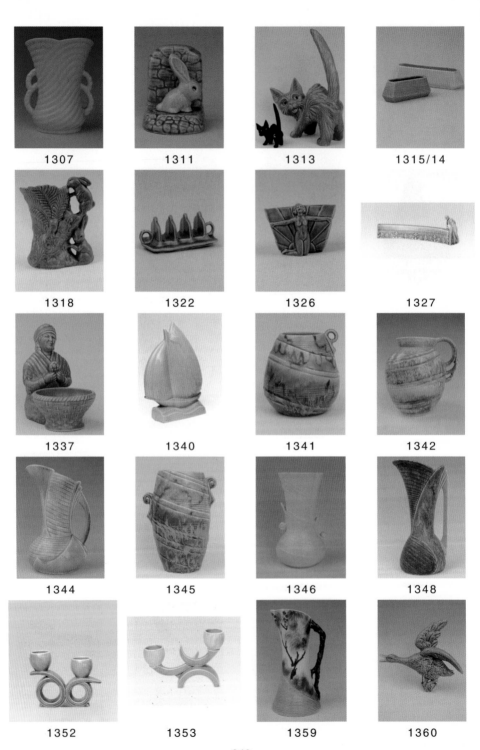

1307

1311

1313

1315/14

1318

1322

1326

1327

1337

1340

1341

1342

1344

1345

1346

1348

1352

1353

1359

1360

1363

1365

1372

1375

1378

1379

1380/78

1382

1384

1385

1391

1393

1394

1395

1396

1402

1404

1415

1418

1420

1426

1431

1433

1435

1438

1439

1452

1455

1457

1463

1466

1473

1479

1481

1494

1500

1510

1513

1514

1546

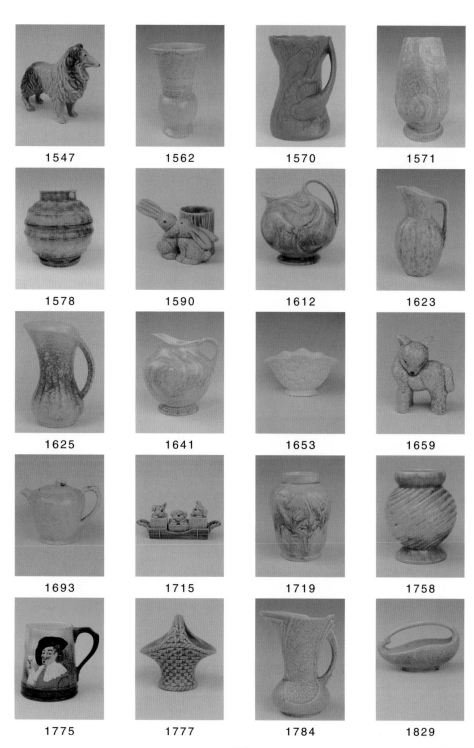

1547

1562

1570

1571

1578

1590

1612

1623

1625

1641

1653

1659

1693

1715

1719

1758

1775

1777

1784

1829

251

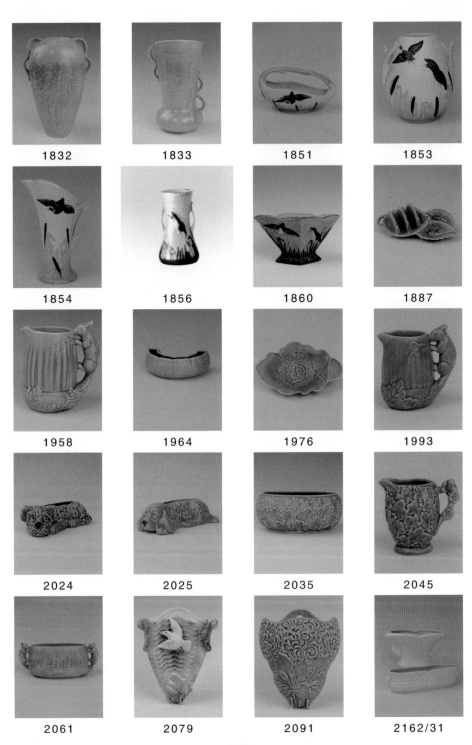

1832

1833

1851

1853

1854

1856

1860

1887

1958

1964

1976

1993

2024

2025

2035

2045

2061

2079

2091

2162/31

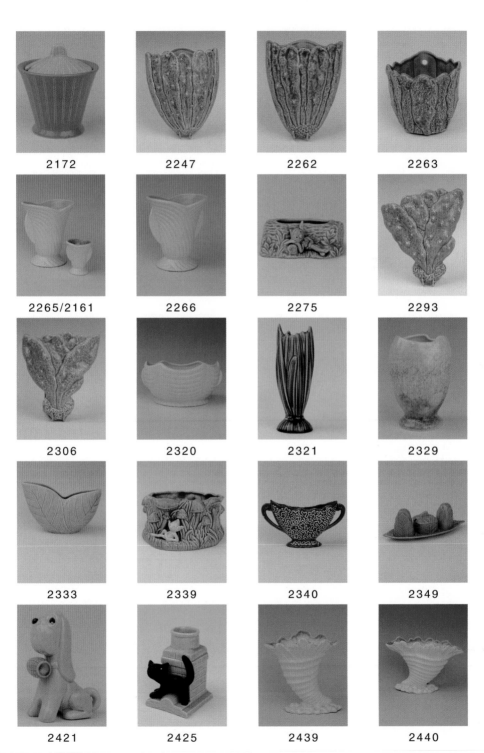

2172

2247

2262

2263

2265/2161

2266

2275

2293

2306

2320

2321

2329

2333

2339

2340

2349

2421

2425

2439

2440

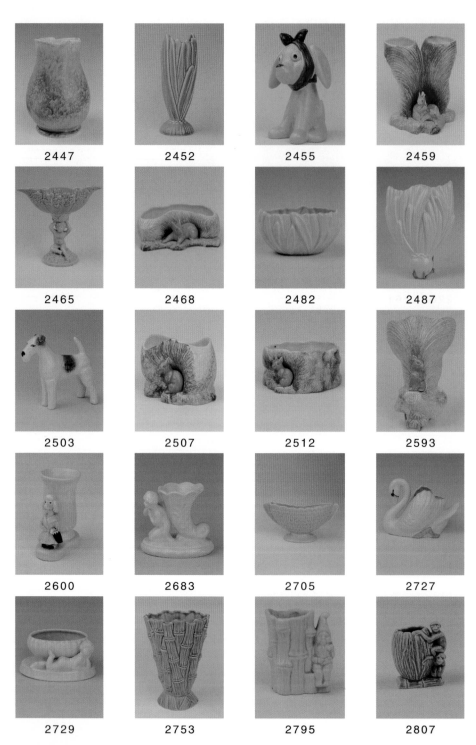

2447

2452

2455

2459

2465

2468

2482

2487

2503

2507

2512

2593

2600

2683

2705

2727

2729

2753

2795

2807

254

2829

2874

2875

2938/50

2951

2954

2962

2981

2993

3001

3032

3093

3098

3110

3128

3191

3209

3210

3214

3215

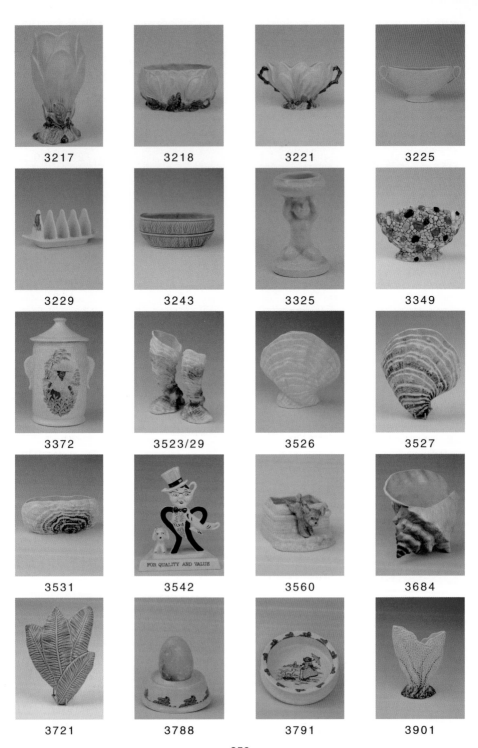

3217

3218

3221

3225

3229

3243

3325

3349

3372

3523/29

3526

3527

3531

3542

FOR QUALITY AND VALUE

3560

3684

3721

3788

3791

3901

3922

3956

4011

4231

4239

4240

4241

4293

4307

4332

4343

4393

4491

4539

4557

4565

4641

4750

4752

4755

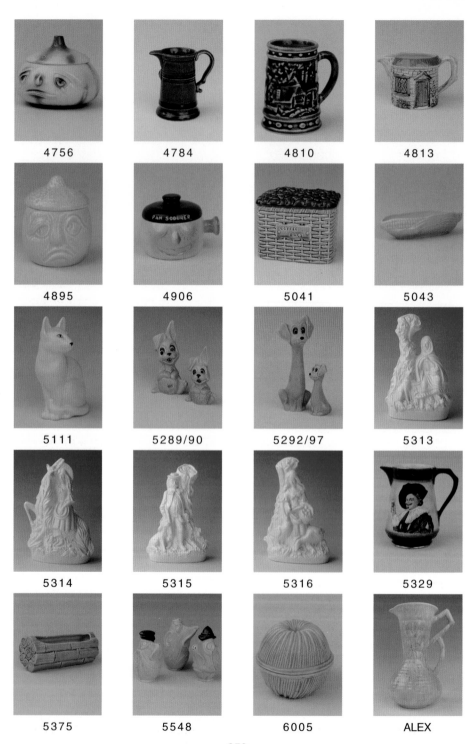

4756

4784

4810

4813

4895

4906

5041

5043

5111

5289/90

5292/97

5313

5314

5315

5316

5329

5375

5548

6005

ALEX

CENTRE	DUCKBILL	F	F142
F170	F477	F582	F583
F585	F688	F73	JUG&BO~1
JUG&BO~2	MIMENTO	NN	NO
PORTLAND	PORTLA~1	ROMAN	'T' PLATE

The Illustrated SylvaC Collectors Handbook is only the briefest of guides and combines the previous two editions of the Sylvac Collectors Handbook Part 1 and Part 2. This book covers mould numbers 1-6128. Published by Georgian Publications PO Box 1449, Bath, BA1 2FF.

Further reading:
Shaw & Copestake The Collectors Guide to Early SylvaC 1894-1939 by Anthony Van Der Woerd, published by Georgian Publications, PO Box 1449, Bath, BA1 2FF

Georgian Publication web site
www.sylvac.org
for purchase and update information.

Are you interested in SylvaC ware?
Do you collect?
Then why not join …

The SylvaC
Collectors Circle

SylvaC always bought
from single items to whole collections

For full details send SAE to:
Mick and Derry Collins
174 Portsmouth Road
Horndean
Hants PO8 9HP
Tel 01705 591725 after 6pm
E-Mail: admin@sylvacclub.com **Website:** www.sylvac.org